# FIRST WORLD wAR
# FLYING ACE

## 20-year Adventure of Harry Chisam
## 1912-1932

by
Andy Milne
and
Margaret Chisam Partington

ISBN: 978-0-9561792-0-3

Second printing with revisions published in 2009 by Margaret Partington
The Hall House, 20 High Street, Datchet  SL3 9EQ

Printed by Launton Digital Press, Green Farm, Fritwell, Oxon  OX27 7QU

Production and design by Trevor Preece: trevor@epic-gb.com
2 Sella Bank, Seascale, Cumbria  CA20 1QU

In loving memory

of

**William Hargrove Chisam**

Born November 15th 1894

Died 16th August 1972

From the Wright Brothers

to the Sopwith Camel,

the RAF and Concorde in one lifetime.

# Taking the Field

Clouds hid the aircraft from the watchers on the ground, but they could hear the engine, a distant growl, then silence, then the growl again. Rain squalls and low cloud had lashed the Yorkshire coast that spring but 14th May 1916 had started out as a good day for flying.

"He's making for Redcar, but he's too far south," Captain Gordon said.

"So what's he doing coming down here?"

"Engine trouble, that's what he's doing and he's looking for somewhere to land, Sergeant Major."

Gordon and his men – who had come out of the tents – gazed up at the craft curving around the sky.

Keeping his opinion of pilots and their infernal machines to himself Sergeant Major Buttress tried to imagine the pilot in the speck above him. How would the man ever pick out a level patch of ground from the tartan of pasture and meadow below? Gordon had made camp near a small river a mile from the village at Marske. Rows of khaki coloured tents quadrangled a level paddock. Over the white-blossomed hawthorn hedge burbled a shallow stream.

"I venture he'll pick out the largest field he can spot."

"Sir, perhaps he'll make for the river meadow."

Gordon had picked the spot because it was near fresh water. Alongside the stream stretched a narrow, straight pasture, rich with buttercups and cattle. He started to compose an order to assemble the men.

However the bellow of the Sergeant Major, clearly audible half a mile away, stopped him.

"Mayday, mayday," Buttress shouted. Raising both arms above him he curled them down to his shoulders, an order to gather on him. Ten seconds later the Sergeant Major and a cohort of infantrymen in various white vests and khaki trousers set off at the double from the camp into the long field over the hedge. At one end stood a bemused herd of cattle.

"Drive them out lads," shouted Buttress. "Baines, open the bally gate first."

Straining through his goggles and leather helmet the pilot looked more closely at the field over the side of his aircraft, a Gnome Caudron bi-plane.

The pilot caught the movement of the black and white cattle far below as the aircraft coughed once more high above the stampede. Then he realised the soldiers were herding the cows out of the field into a paddock. Although not overly wide it was long and straight. Being near water, he supposed, it would be reasonably flat. The engine fired and as gently as he'd been taught he eased up the nose, desperate to gain height.

"He's flying away, the damn fool," said Gordon, panting up behind Buttress.

"With respect, sir, he's a naval pilot, sir, he's trying to turn in to the wind."

The engine cut out altogether during the turn. Trees lined the stream. Missing the oaks and letting the wind lift him down gently was the key to survival. The wind was fresh from the coast, blowing parallel with the stream. The engine fired again and the pilot swung round for the final approach. Pulling mightily he managed to level up above the fields.

The men in the field looked up and then looked at the Sergeant Major. Buttress said, "Stay where you are by the trees."

The pilot seemed to float on the thermals as the plane droned in low over the meadow. What looked like a flat field from the air had a series of ridges: low hummocks rolled up by centuries of ploughing that rippled the very earth the soldiers and airman defended. The pilot could see nothing of this as the grass raced along just below his wings.

The plane put down and careered along the field, then hit a ridge and jumped in the air. The engine raced and the craft, ungainly on the ground, plunged down into the grass. The propeller bit the rough sod and the craft veered in a waltz towards the trees.

Captain Gordon looked on horrified. It is never easy to watch a man die, he reflected. Then a strange thing happened. As the aircraft switched back over the next ridge, bucking now like a switchback ride, the pilot popped out of the plane like a champagne cork. The man simply rocketed into the air and plummeted down to the ground. The plane carried on and crashed into the trees. Gordon looked at the mangled wreckage of the plane and then at the heap of clothes all but hidden by the grass. The pilot lay very still on the ground. Buttress and a posse of troopers sprinted across to him.

"Don't move him, lads, don't move him," he shouted.

But the pilot had already sat up. His legs splayed in front of him, blood streaming down his face from a gash in his forehead. He looked down at his left hand and flexed it carefully. The minor operation he'd had on his hand seemed OK.

The air became very still, the troopers stood peering at the man – little more than a boy – who had droned into their midst. The metal of the aircraft groaned and pinked in the sunshine. A cow lowed over the hedge. Dragonflies danced and dived above the stream. The horrors of the war in France seemed a long way away.

"Are you at HMS President?" Captain Gordon said, guessing he was on a training flight from the base at Redcar.

"I met the President once," said the pilot and then appeared to blackout.

The officer decided to carry him back to the tents. A messenger would be despatched to the base. But the pilot regained consciousness and refused to be picked up by the men. Kneeling on all fours he was unceremoniously sick into the lush, green grass.

Squatting down beside him the Sergeant Major said, "Who are you? Do you remember?"

Before replying the pilot clambered to his feet, leaning on Buttress for support. He took several deep breaths and exhaled through a nose foamed with blood. Seeing the pips on Gordon's shoulders he snapped to attention and saluted.

"Flight Sub-Lieutenant Chisam, Royal Naval Air Service. At your service, sir."

The Sergeant Major caught him up neatly with one ham-like arm as the pilot stumbled.

"Right ho, Mr Chisam – I think we'd best get you home," the Captain said.

---

William Hargrove Chisam was flying a French bi-plane, a Caudron, powered by a Gnome engine. The Caudron G.III had been developed in May 1913. This particular aircraft was built by Le Crotoy and had been used by the RNAS at

The remains of a French
Caudron. An inscription on
the back of the photo says,
"The careless pilot? Me!"
Redcar, spring 1916.

Harry's crash on 26th July,
1917, in France

Chingford and Eastchurch – where it crashed on 12th January 1916. Once repaired it was sent north to Redcar. Mr Chisam's career, which could so easily have ended in a field in Yorkshire, would go on to light up the annals of the Great War. His courage and fortitude informed hundreds of combat missions flown over the mired battle fields of France and the U-boat-haunted seas off Scotland and southern England. He accounted for seven kills and qualified as an air ace. Harry, as his friends called him, was a founder member of the Royal Air Force, a guarantor of the freedom of the skies over Britain from that day to this.

"I see you were forced down by engine trouble," said Commander Fawcett.

"Yes sir, I'm sorry about the plane, sir."

"Aeroplane, Chisam." Then the commander looked up from his papers.

"Look, what you did, bringing her down safely and making a crash landing in that field was very well done. You understand the point, lieutenant, don't you?"

Harry Chisam didn't and thought it best to say so.

"No sir, not quite, sir."

He stood in front of the oak desk. The squadron commander hadn't asked him to sit down and he looked at the three pipes laid out to the left of a much used green blotter. The desk had been inlaid with a scraping of red leather. Books and maps and atlases piled up around a central clearing on which lay the medical report.

"The lesson is you landed safely – albeit with cuts and bruises and concussion. The plane we can repair, or in this case, simply replace. Do you understand?" Suddenly he stood up and walked over to the window looking out at two sailors painting the kerb stones round the camp perimeter road white.

"We cannot quickly replace pilots. Every second of experience you gain has to help us. Throwing it away in a water meadow outside Marske hardly helps the war effort does it flight lieutenant?"

"No sir, I see, sir."

Fawcett wrote out a Certificate for Wounds and Hurts. Chisam, he wrote, "was injured on 14th May 1916 by being forced to land owing to engine trouble and crashing the machine on uneven ground. He was thrown out on to the grass and sustained shock and small abrasions and bruises about the face. He was not unconscious – but showed signs of slight concussion, i.e. vomiting and headaches. There were no other signs of any injury."

"Now, you suffered concussion and vomiting. All clear now?"

"Yes sir, I'm quite recovered, thank you, sir."

"Yes well I've marked you up for a week's leave. Go back to your home, let your mother look after you for a week or so, I'm sure she'll make a better job of it than the Admiralty."

**Certificate
for Wounds
and Hurts.**

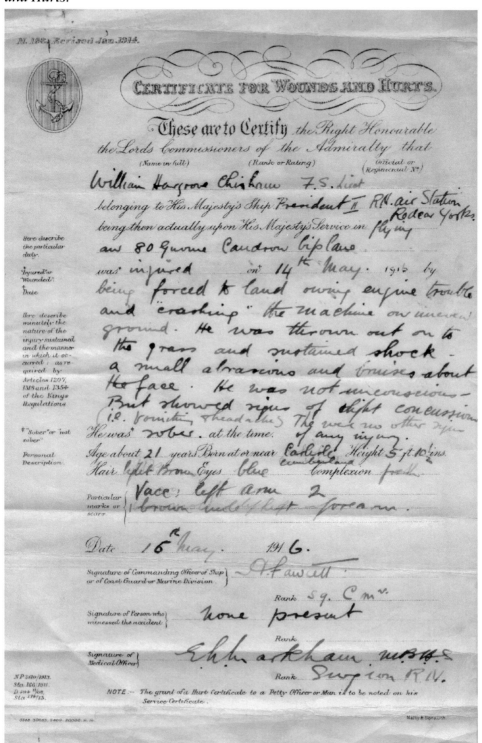

*Harry as a Sea Scout in 1905.*

*Harry's first trip to sea on the River Hamble in 1905.*

# Home Leave

A policeman in a raincape saluted as he left the railway station. Rain soaked down the red sandstone and a cart jolted past piled high with furniture. Harry Chisam stepped back to avoid being sprayed by a puddle. Surprised at the policeman's salute he pressed into the wind and rain, turned up his great coat and headed down the street to his parents' hotel. The smell of fried bacon, polish and cigars welcomed him as he flitted through a side door, keen not to be spotted. In an office with a glass door he could see a woman with her back to him talking to a man in blue trousers and a red, brass-buttoned waistcoat. They heard the click of the door and the man snapped ramrod straight. Oh dear, thought Harry Chisam, he's going to salute again. "Good morning, sir, very pleased to see you, sir."

"Thank you Smith, it's good to be home." His mother simply flung her arms round him, hanging on to him as if the very weight of her slight frame would keep him anchored to the ground. Smith, with a career of master-key discretion behind him, slipped through the glass door. The news, he felt, deserved a much wider dissemination.

"We received your letter, but what happened, a crash?"

"Is father here? I could tell you together, it's nothing too serious. You should have seen the plane!"

"How much longer do they think the war will last?"

This was the question increasingly at the forefront of all thinking about a war so glibly embarked upon in August 1914. The great armies of the empires had become bogged down in the mud of Flanders and northern France. Similarly, soldiers of both sides wheeled and died across the plains and forests of Poland and the south. Harry Chisam had been born into a world dominated by empires. The British Empire compassed Canada, India, much of Africa and Asia, New Zealand and Australia. The French Empire stretched across Algeria and Tunisia, the deserts of Africa and the teeming jungles of Indo-China. However, history is never static. The Spanish Empire had faded, South American republics like Chile and Argentina declaring independence in the early part of the 19th century. In central Europe, a newly emboldened Prussia had unified the German empire and chaffed for new markets and raw materials. To the south, the Austro-Hungarian Empire knitted together Slavic dukedoms and alpine principalities. The Emperor Franz Joseph had ruled since 1848. Further south, still, the failing Ottoman Empire reached out from Turkey, snaking the cruel arm of the Sultanate around the eastern Mediterranean.

The origins of the Great War lie as much in the friction between rival empires as in the yearning of sovereign peoples to be free. In June 1914 the heir to the throne of Austria-Hungary, Archduke Franz Ferdinand, with his wife, Sophia, insisted on travelling to the town of Sarajevo in Bosnia-Herzegovina, a Balkan province once occupied by Turkey but annexed by Austria in 1908. Travelling through Sarajevo, Archduke Franz Ferdinand and Sophia were assassinated by Gavrilo Princip, a terrorist in the pay of Belgrade, capital of Serbia. Of itself the incident, which horrified Austria-Hungary, should have led to no more than diplomatic protest and the trial of the conspirators. However, the Serbian military was widely implicated in the plot. Austria-Hungary demanded action and a wide ranging enquiry. Years of rivalry between the powers burst open. Dissatisfied by the Serbian response to the assassination Austria-Hungary mobilised and declared war on Serbia on 28th July 1914. This in turn precipitated a Russian mobilisation – Russia was a guarantor of Serbian independence seeking to protect a fellow Orthodox and Slavic power. As the summer boiled on, Russia's action meant Germany mobilised, alarmed that an Austrian-Russian conflagration would catch it unprepared. Germany's Kaiser, Wilhelm II, had known the murdered Franz Ferdinand well and mourned the tragic death of the young couple. Russia was allied with France. Belgium was neutral and guaranteed by Britain.

Germany declared war on Russia and then France at the beginning of August. Victory for Germany in any European war depended on knocking out France and facing off Russia. The von Schlieffen plan was put into action. German forces under Moltke invaded Luxembourg and Belgium and swept into France. With Belgian neutrality violated, Great Britain declared war on Germany on 4th August.

The initial stages of the war seemed a continuation of the sabre rattling that had bedevilled European politics for the past 40 years. However, the advent of the machine gun, heavy artillery and gas meant the skirmishes so lightly embarked upon would become the most horrific land war ever waged in the dark annals of military history. Young men going off to join up along with all their friends and brothers from a particular street or village gave small thought to this. What soldiers they knew were dare-devil men who had fought wars in mountain and desert in the far flung outposts of empire. It would be an end-of-summer adventure; they'd be home to get the harvest in, certainly by Christmas.

As Harry Chisam sat down to tea with his family in May 1916 neither he nor his parents could guess the war had entered stalemate and would last another two and half years.

"I knew I wouldn't make it back to the naval air station in time so I looked for a place to land. Trouble with Yorkshire is the roads are all winding and narrow. What you need is a field."

"A long, straight field," said his father.

"Yes, long, straight and flat," Harry said looking at his hand as it lay on the white table cloth. Then he picked up a cup and lifted it to his lips. The twinge was back in his hand but it was OK and he knew he could disguise it from the naval surgeons. Playing the piano later would help.

"It's good to have you back. We thought we wouldn't see you again for a very long time," his mother said.

"A very long time, Harry," echoed his younger sister, Elsie. "When you went to Canada I used to forget you'd gone and lay a place for you."

"I know; Mum told me in a letter. I used to imagine that place setting when I was away in Canada and it made me feel much better, almost like I'd brought you along with me," and he smiled at Elsie. Coming home to Carlisle was an unexpected bonus of the war for Harry Chisam. He had left Britain for a new life in Canada in 1912.

"You were always restless ever since that Boy Scout trip on the river Hamble," said his mother.

"No bad thing in a man, restlessness," said Mr Chisam, a solid hotel proprietor. The Chisams owned the eponymous hotel in Carlisle, the Viaduct Hotel, a grocery store and a chocolate drinking house in Whitehaven.

*Harry at Victoria Road, Carlisle, in 1896.*

*Harry and siblings at the Viaduct Hotel. Left to right: Sessford, Elsie, Edith and Hargrove.*

*Harry at 2½.*

*The Chisams at Eskdale Green, Cumberland.*
*Grandfather Methodist Preacher and family.*

*Harry with his sisters Edith and Elsie, taken at Edith and Robert Clark's wedding.*

*Harry sailed to Canada
on the Corsican on
7th March 1912.*

*Norse Range – the Chisam family home for 50 years, built
in 1909 by Harry's grandfather, in Seascale, Cumberland.*

Born on 15th November 1894 at Carlisle, William Hargrove Chisam emigrated to Canada on 7th March 1912.

"We watched you waving your handkerchief – you held it higher and waved it longer than all the rest," said his father, William Chisam. "You must tell us again how you got on. I mean you were lucky to get out of that soap factory."

"He was lucky to get there at all. I mean the SS Corsican made it. Suppose he'd gone on the Titanic." His mother hardly liked to dwell on the perils of Atlantic sea crossings.

"They are on the whole very safe, dear, compared with horses and motor cars and railway trains," said Mr Chisam.

Harry Chisam had set sail on the SS Corsican from Liverpool, landing in Nova Scotia, from whence he travelled by train overland to Calgary. The Titanic, which sailed after the Corsican, sunk in April 1912. How could he get across to his parents and siblings the cheerfulness and sense of high adventure of the other emigrants? Thousands of men and women left Britain's shores to make a new life in Canada and the United States.

"I'd like to hear more about the police, the Mounties in Edmonton," said his elder brother, Sessford, who would himself serve with distinction in the Great War. "I read they are being reformed and enlarged. Quite unusual; a continent-wide police force."

"Hargrove, honestly, first you nearly take the Titanic, then you get blown to smithereens in a soap factory and then you go and work for a frontier police force, hardly safe and sound," said Edith, his elder sister. Despite her poise and severe stature she had a soft spot for her younger brother and loved to pull his leg.

"Frontier police force, Edith? Like the one here in Carlisle I suppose! I think it was akin to getting into the eye of the storm," said Harry amiably. "Best go right to the root of the trouble and sort it out – much safer."

His father looked up. Suddenly he seemed older and more tired. "Is that why you're flying? Is that the philosophy that took you away up into the sky?"

"I'll tell you all about it over the next few days. What do you think Elsie?"

"Well, we've all weekend for that, haven't we?"

"Shall we go down to Norse Range?" This was the house built in 1909 by Harry Chisam's grandfather, Jonathan Chisam, on the Cumberland coast at Seascale.

Later that Saturday afternoon, getting off the small train at the station, Harry Chisam breathed deeply. Sunlight dappled the sea and two boys bowled hoops in the dusty street. "Where ever I've been, Dad, coming here will always feel like coming home." Instead of objecting that the family home was in Carlisle, his father beamed and clapped his son on his shoulder. He looked out across the sea and considered the five thousand miles this particular naval officer had travelled to fight for his country. Mr Chisam suddenly felt very proud.

*Harry's sister Elsie in 1921.*

*Spring 1912 at Nonsees Ranch, Blaine Lake, Canada.*

*Harry's shack on the ranch.*

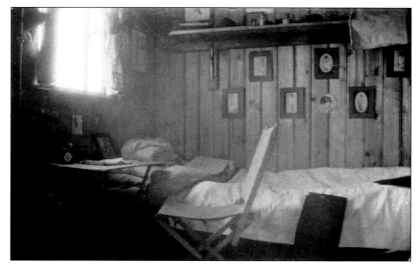

# Police Action

"We have to leave now, we have to get out of the building. Do it now." The elderly Chinese woman did not understand. She turned back to her work at the tools bench. Ally Shaw shouted, "Get her out now, Harry. It'll blow any minute." The livid glow from the boiler lit up the dim interior of the soap factory. Steam shrilled from a hundred shuddering rivets.

Harry Chisam took the woman by the sleeve and pointed at the rest of the staff tearing off pinafores and backing uncertainly towards the double doors that let out of the factory into the midday sun. The whine from the boiler reached a new tempo. "Will you come with me?" he said smiling. "Pretty girl like you shouldn't be here on her own." The woman was in her fifties, part of an immigrant family, seeking fortune far from the Pacific. She let herself be lead away. Harry quickened his pace, or tried to, but the woman was ungainly on her feet and kept looking back. Shaw had disappeared back into the factory. Great tubs of soap stood about. Outside several Chinese labourers were leading the horses away. The animals knew better than the Chinese woman something was deeply wrong. The shrilling on the boiler escape valve screamed up another octave. Suddenly Ally Shaw came charging through the door. The boiler piped a last frantic farewell.

"Get down, Harry, get down." With one enormous arm he swept them to the ground and at the same time the tremendous pressure forced its way out of the boiler. The explosion blew off the roof. Flaming timbers rocketed into the air crashing down around the three of them. Flocks of birds burst into the air from the trees nearby. The horses galloped madly round and round the paddock. The workforce, with a commendable promptness born of long experience, had thrown themselves to the ground. The explosion was not severe but smoke poured through a hole in the roof.

Later that morning old man Anderson pushed back his hat. "I hate to see you go, but the whole damn thing needs to be rebuilt and I ain't got the funds." The soap factory was out of action.

———— • — ————

Two Royal Canadian Mounted Police – resplendent in scarlet coats and broad brimmed brown hats – walked their horses carefully down the street.

"Know how to ride a horse?" Ally Shaw asked.

"I started out over here working on a farm at Blaine Lake, Saskatchewan, so yes, I know how to ride a horse."

"What happened?

"The horse and the cattle had a bit of trouble."

"You stampeded a herd of beef cattle?"

"Well it wasn't quite as bad as that – sounds worse than it actually was. They just took off."

"Not quite the Chisholm Trail though?"

"No, at least the farmer punched me out – nearly broke my jaw. So I guess it was the wild west."

"Goodness, a regular cowboy! Not having much luck are you? I mean, stampedes, fighting, explosions. All you need now is a war."

Ally Shaw, a tall thin Ulsterman who was to become a life long friend, said, "Let's join the police then – the Mounties."

The recruiting sergeant was unhelpful. Shaw stood in the police post doorway looking out across the street. A man came in from the room behind the desk. "It's no good, the boss wants the proceedings transcribed and Millie can't keep up. Keeps stopping and saying pardon me, sir, but how are you spelling that? Thing is the judge can't spell neither."

The sergeant looked up at the would-be Mountie leaning over the desk again. "What is it now?"

"Excuse me, but I couldn't help over-hearing – I trained as a stenographer and a clerk back in Cumberland. Half the job is common sense. I can transcribe proceedings for you."

The sergeant looked up and pursed his lips, then he scratched the back of his neck and came to a decision. "OK, follow me, son."

"Where you lodging?"

"I just arrived in Manitoba this afternoon," said Harry as they walked across the street.

"What you have to realise, son, is Manitoba, right here in 1912, is still frontier territory. Settlers, trappers, prospectors and the natives, we have a working population very different from back home. Folks can make it rich here and it is competitive, just see if it ain't."

WINNIPEG TRIBUNE 1913

### RULING OF THE COURT.

September 19th, 1913.

In the matter of The King vs. Ings. Three charges of Horse Stealing and Theft.

Mr. J. Allen, deputy attorney-general, notifies the court that the crown intend to take over the prosecution in connection with the three remaining charges against Fred W. Ings which are on the docket this day.

Mr. Allen also stated that the crown take this step not on account of any incompetency or improper conduct on the part of Mr. Bonnar, who has had charge of the prosecution up to this time.

The court rules that the crown has the right to take charge of the prosecution.

HUGH J. MACDONALD,
Police Magistrate.

Certified correct,
W. H. CHISAM,
Court Reporter.

*Police Court Winnipeg. Harry was Court Reporter from November 1912 to November 1915.*

*Winnipeg, Canada, in 1912.*

*Harry is second from left. Canada in October 1913.*

*Harry with two girl friends in Ambrain Park, Canada.*

*Harry in Canada.*

*Harry in the Canadian Rockies.*

*Near Edmonton in October 1914.*

The law courts in Winnipeg, the bustling province capital, sported a sorry progression of drunks, murderers, cut throats and thieves. Human frailty has no limits. "We got 'em all here, son. Man needs a strong stomach in court Monday mornings."

Yet the grandeur of the lakes and tundra was matched only by the outgoing friendliness of Canadians themselves and the immigrants who quickly adopted their cheerful values. Arctic fresh air blew away the doubts of a previous life.

---

When war was declared in August 1914 most people expected it to be over in a matter of months. "They'll be back by Christmas," old men observed as the new recruits marched down dusty, summer streets to the beat of a drum.

In Winnipeg, Harry Chisam's initial reaction to the war probably shared the conventional view that this was a series of wheeling skirmishes that would soon be wrapped up by monocled diplomats in gilded halls. Wars were commonplace. The US government had fought a disagreeable series of wars with the Native Americans right up until the end of the nineteenth century. The Mexican Revolution had descended into the Pancho Villa–Diaz civil war two years before. The Japanese had fought Russia in 1904-5. War was regarded as far less of a crisis than it is today. Soldiers were rarely seen in action by the public. They fought and died far away from home, their graves unnumbered cobbles on the roads of empire. Few in Europe foresaw the sheer scale and carnage of the Great War. Indeed the initial battles of autumn 1914 were wheeling manoeuvres by each side aimed at outflanking the opposition and cutting off the opposing army.

Following the Schlieffen Plan the German Army invaded Belgium. Despite valiant fighting at Liège, the Belgians were overwhelmed and the population harshly treated. The Germans swept on to the sea. Schlieffen's aim had been to turn the flank of the French armies invading through Flanders. Indeed the Germans came within 25 miles of Paris – observers later claimed they could see the Eiffel Tower on a clear day. The Germans and the Allies fought and counter fought at the Battle of the Marne. At sea the mighty British navy seemed ominously out-manoeuvred. In September 1914 *HMS Aboukir, Hogue* and *Cressy* were all sunk by a submarine, U-boat number *U-9*. Soldiers in Western Europe dug in, constructing a series of trenches that stretched from the Swiss border to the North Sea. Switzerland remained neutral and its neutrality was respected unlike that of Belgium. By Christmas, it was far from over.

At the end of September 1914 Harry Chisam left Manitoba, getting a better job at the Magistrates Court in Edmonton, capital of Alberta. Early in the New Year he had a conversation with Ally Shaw.

"Over by Christmas? What do you think?"

"It's just getting under way, that's what I think."

"Yes, the Canadians are raising a third contingent."

"Think we should go?"

"Oh there's no doubt about that," said Shaw.

"I thought of going back and joining up."

"Trouble is our age – parental consent and all that rot."

Harry nodded gloomily "Are we rushing off because it's an adventure and an escape? That's what one's parents may think."

*Young man about town! Harry in Edmonton while working in the law courts...*

"That suits their point of view at any rate."

"Or is it a matter of fighting for what a man believes in. Quite simply I want to serve my country."

"I agree. Remember Belgium."

Both agreed the war was far from over. Talking it through the next point was how best one could help the war effort.

"I believe the best bet would be to try for a commission in the Canadian army," said Shaw.

"I had it in mind to go for the Navy – I spent a few weeks as a scout on a sailing rig in the river Hamble."

"That'll impress the Admiralty, I'm sure."

"OK then, what about flying?"

Shaw looked at his friend in puzzlement. "Flying? What you mean in one of those aeroplanes?"

"Well yes, dash it. I don't mean hanging about in one of those dirigible balloon whatsits. I mean an aircraft."

In his hands he fingered a letter that had arrived that morning from his sister, Elsie, in England. Even after a year he didn't feel he knew Ally Shaw well enough to tell him what had inspired him to fly.

"You know Smith, Jack Smith, who works in the hotel? Well he knows how to set bones," Elsie wrote. "He said it's simply a matter of splinting the bone in a straight-line and the flesh and bone itself knows how to grow again. In fact he says a broken bone when it is set properly and knits together forms a join that is stronger than the original limb was." Harry could almost hear his younger sister's breathless excitement as she described the blackbird which had crashed into the unhelpfully pristine kitchen windows behind the hotel. "I saw him flopping about in the yard, quite unable to take off."

Elsie Chisam rushed out of the kitchen where she been sipping hot chocolate.

Quite fearlessly she knelt down and cradled the injured bird in her hands and picked him up. Smith appeared at her elbow. "Better give him over to me Miss."

"Why what will you do?"

"Put him out of his misery, bird that can't fly is no bird at all. He's not free if you get my meaning – that's his purpose."

One of the Chisam family's abiding Methodist-based philosophies was that by faith and hard work you could achieve almost anything. "Princes and paupers may forget, but that's how we built an empire, by faith and hard work. We travailed and were heavy laden," Mr Chisam pronounced, a majestic figure who preached and lived the Gospel with Pauline thoroughness.

"Thank you Mr Smith but I mean to make him well again. It's a broken wing." She peeped inside her folded hands. "It's his right wing, I think."

Smith peered at the bird.

"I think he must have turned at the last minute, Miss. That's why he broke his wing and not his neck."

"Well if it was a human we'd get his bone set. I'm going to see father and we can have his physician call on us." The girl was about to walk off complete with blackbird.

"No, listen, Miss, I wouldn't do that." Smith understood the pressures on his employer rather more sympathetically than his daughter.

He summoned the boot boy and demanded off him kindling sticks and the hand axe. "We'll need hair ribbons, Miss, old ones your mother won't miss." Patiently the trio cut down minute splints. With a tenderness normally better concealed, Smith splinted and trussed the blackbird.

"I'm afraid the shock of all this might kill him, we'll have to see. If he gets through the first night he'll get home – that's what we used to say in the army in Africa. He's a fine looking bird isn't he?"

The blackbird watched them, unblinking, his head and orange beak poking through silk swaddling clothes.

"I had to get up early and dig for worms, I fed him slugs, too, and bits of bread," she went on.

Harry Chisam, engrossed, read the long letter through as he would dozens more like it in Canadian coffee shops and police stations; in French and Belgian cafés and on a dozen air fields, too. The great day came and Smith pronounced the bone should have knitted.

"We put him down in the garden – he's called Oliver – and he hopped about with his wings folded. Then he jumped and flapped and took off and then set down again. Then he glided from one end of the lawn to the other. I looked round to tell Smith – and when I looked back he'd taken off, gone."

Smith smiled broadly. Elsie said, "There you are then, he's free now – free as a bird, Mr Smith."

Harry Chisam folded the letter and looked up. A man with a horse and cart was walking up the road. Two Indians were leaning on a fence across the road, arms folded, talking; a timeless wisdom etched upon their faces. Above them, Chisam noticed, birds lined the telegraph wires.

"Smith thinks the first day or two will be difficult as Oliver has to learn to fly again. But I think he will and I think he'll be all right. Oliver's ever so brave – I don't think he'd have pulled through if he wasn't."

Harry Chisam and Ally Shaw started to read up on flying, investigating the

Wright brothers, Curtiss, the great efforts the French had made and the exploits of the American military already experimenting with guns fired from aeroplanes.

That June, 1915, the Saskatchewan River flooded its banks washing into Edmonton and making over two thousand people homeless. Timber businesses, sawmills and foundries were simply washed away. The police and the law courts were kept busy with looters, or more usually, passers-by who had helped themselves.

After a long day at work Harry Chisam would meet Ally Shaw for coffee. Already Alberta's strict anti-alcohol laws made it difficult to buy a drink.

"You can see how easy it is to roll up civilisation," said Ally as they looked down at the newspaper folded on the table in front of them. "I mean take a natural disaster, a flood or earthquake and people revert to acting like cavemen."

"I don't know which poses more of a threat, the river Saskatchewan or the politicians."

"I know; hell, Harry, I could murder a cold beer. How do you stick it listening to all that guff in court all day?"

"I like listening to people, listen long enough and they'll tell you the truth. I think deep down most people are good. We're Methodists, the Chisams, bible believing Methodists, but I have never really accepted the teachings on original sin, at least not in their traditional form. We may behave appallingly. But if we're made in the image of God then I think we always know what we should be doing. We always know we could be good."

"Try telling that to the Kaiser."

"I could, but the question is would he listen?"

Harry Chisam first applied for a commission in the fledgling Canadian Aviation Corps. However, this corps was later abandoned. His next move was to seek a Royal Flying Corps commission, writing to the War Office in February 1915. The reply was hardly encouraging. "If you return to England at some future date at your own expense, you can then renew your application when it will receive consideration. But no promise can be made that you will be employed in the Royal Flying Corps."

In March Chisam applied for a commission in the Canadian Army. Martin Bruton, Chief Constable in Regina, Alberta, recommended his young friend. "I had every opportunity to note the quiet and capable manner in which he always discharged his duties ..." Bruton wrote. "He now informs me that he is anxious to obtain a commission in one of the battalions about to be formed and I have great pleasure in recommending him." Bruton knew and liked the self-effacing Englishman, a quiet and level-headed presence in the hustle and bustle of the courts.

"I am confident he would make a good officer," Hugh MacDonald, a magistrate, agreed in a letter to Major General Sam Hughes of the Canadian Militia, dated 12th April 1915.

Chisam's determination to fly grew that summer. It seemed the more obstacles put in his way, the more he resolved to overcome them. The history of the Canadian Aviation Corps – whose three members sailed with the first contingent, was brief. The corps was wound up for the duration and thereafter Canadian pilots served with the British air forces – of which there were two.

"My father's against it. You have to teach yourself to fly. The flying schools are full and then we have to pay for it all to boot. Honestly!"

"Ah but think of it Ally, determination, grit, it's exactly what will win us the war."

Harry Chisam had savings totalling 1,000 dollars. Whimsically he imagined he could make a few dollars playing the piano in a bar between flights.

# American Girl

The plane trembled as it moved forward across the rough, wet grass. Harry Chisam tugged his cloth cap round backwards on his head and brushed the sweat out of his eyes. Despite the winter chill on the morning air he felt hot and taking a deep breath watched the instructor, now standing clear. The pilot sat on the lower wing itself completely exposed to the elements – no one expected to have to stay in the air for very long. The aeroplanes were Wright 'B' models powered by a four cylinder engine clamped to the wing by four bolts. The engine juddered the wing and the pilot had to hold on tight, wedging his feet on the protruding foot rest. Cycle chains carried the motive power of the engine to the twin propellers.

The instructor raised his hand and then dropped it. Harry Chisam trundled forward. The craft jarred from side to side, the wings seemed to shake to their own rhythm. As he gained speed Harry Chisam eased the craft into the air. "I didn't realise I'd done it for a second or two but then I saw the grass flashing by under me. Already just a few feet into the air I felt good, free." The craft flew straight and low and he brought her in to land just a few hundred feet from where he'd taken off. Exhilarated he snatched off his cap and jumped down.

"Well done, partner," said the instructor chasing up.

The engine stuttered and cut out. "Let's go see if Ally Shaw can match you!" said the instructor. "Then we'll head on in to eat."

A gust of cold air caused the instructor to look up. A local man, he knew it carried snow. Already the flying lessons had been curtailed by bad weather. Privately he knew the rookies would not get through before the onset of winter. He pushed back his Stetson. The old man could worry about that.

---

Robertson, the waiter, paused at the table full of young men again. "Everything OK, gentlemen?" Outside flakes of snow settled lightly on the street. It was now very cold.

Yes, everything was fine, they chorused. Unconvinced he reappeared with a metal coffee pot. The flying students from the Huffman Prairie often sat together at the Algonquin Grill. Some had flown at dawn. It had been still and cold early that morning. Now a north wind was funnelling down from Canada. "The food was always excellent," said Harry Chisam, "but that morning we hardly noticed it."

The weather was closing in and there'd be no more flying that year at Dayton. "You'll have to wait for the spring, I guess," the instructor had said as a group of them wheeled the bi-plane into its hangar. "Mr Wright can't simply shoo you through without you really knowing how to fly. You'll just be killing yourselves. Mr Wright has one hell of a conscience, I can tell you."

"Yes I know, he's a good man," said Harry Chisam. He recalled his initial interview with Orville Wright and the man who pioneered aviation saying, "We'd like to help you son, so yes, you do all I tell you and I'll teach you how to fly."

Aviation was barely ten years old when war was declared. Yet tales of the Wright brothers' powered flight had fired the imagination of a generation. The French in particular had pursued the idea and the military had been quick to see the advantages of powered craft in the air. Initially this would simply be an aid to observation. However, the Italian, Guido Douhet, said, "The sky is about to become another battlefield." Louis Bleriot flew across the English Channel in 1909. The British had no air industry to speak of, relying on French imports like the Caudron. The Royal Flying Corps was formed in 1912, mainly to help observe enemy movements. The navy, not to be out done, realised it too needed aircraft to help scout the seas. The Royal Naval Air Service was formed in January 1914. Both services would be merged to form the Royal Air Force in April 1918. At the outbreak of war streams of young men wanted to fly. In Canada they were told only qualified aviators could join. Eventually Ally Shaw and Harry Chisam, 1,000 miles from the coast, hit upon the idea of joining the Royal Naval Air Service. The RNAS seemed much better organised and indeed in Canada was organised around the Curtiss aviation school in Toronto. The Toronto Curtiss School opened in May 1915, using flying boats and Curtiss JN-3 biplanes. However, the queue to join and train was a long one. Emboldened by the progress of the war and the knowledge gleaned from his reading Harry Chisam applied for entry to the RNAS as did Ally Shaw. On 15th August Chisam received a letter from the Naval Service in Ottawa. "You are hereby accepted as a candidate for the Royal Naval Air Service. Upon obtaining your aero club certificate, you will be entered as a Probationary Flight Sub Lieutenant. In the meantime you should keep the Department informed of your progress."

However there was a further hurdle. Harry would not be 21 until 15th November 1915. He needed his father's consent to join the forces and had telegraphed Carlisle, early in May. The reply prompt and to the point read, "Cannot consent await letter." In fact, Mr Chisam senior duly consented. "I had made an application to Ottawa and been instructed to proceed to Equimaly in Vancouver Island, British Columbia for interview and medical. The interview was favourable. I was told by a non-service doctor I would need an operation on my hand, then I'd be OK – the cost of the op was 100 dollars. I had proceeded to Ottawa together with Ally Shaw and flannelled my way through acceptance." Joining both the Royal Flying Corps and the RNAS had one steep obstacle – the would-be pilots had to pay for their own training at civilian flying schools – and were only judged suitable for engagement once in possession of an aero-club certificate.

Shaw and Chisam had decided to enrol at the Wright Brothers' Flying School in Dayton, Ohio across the border in the United States.

"We thought it would speed things up and a number of British flyers were doing the same. That particular morning it looked like it would be too late."

Shaw and Chisam left Canada in September and enrolled in Wright's flying school at Huffman Prairie, Dayton, Ohio at the beginning of October. Chisam signed a training agreement with the Wright Company which was itself signed by Orville Wright. His brother Wilbur had died of typhoid fever two years before. The cost of the course was 250 dollars. To pass, the would-be pilot had to fly 400 feet and land safely.

The Wright brothers are generally credited with sustaining the first heavier-than-air human flight on 17th December 1903. For would-be aviators their approach was refreshingly thorough and secure. The Wrights measured, checked and experimented, cautiously and without undue risk. They made use of kites, gliders and wind tunnels. The system of aircraft controls they developed made fixed wing flight possible. Importantly the Wrights had learnt how to control pitch, roll and yaw. By

*Harry's flying school classmates in 1915.*
*Harry is third on left in the middle row.*

*Harry Chisam, RNAS.*

# TRANS-ATLANTIC CABLEGRAM.

FORM T D R E

**CANADIAN PACIFIC TELEGRAPH**

| No. | Time | | JAS. KENT, Manager Telegraphs. |
|-----|------|---|---|
| **Check** | | | |
| **Route Via** | | | May 9th 1915. 191 |

Send the following Cablegram **"Via Commercial Cables,"** subject to the terms and conditions printed on the back hereof, which are agreed to.

To      CHISAM'S HOTEL    CARLISLE   Eng

| | | |
|---|---|---|
| applying | aviation | corp |
| send | birth | certificate |
| and | your | consent |
| direct | secretary | department |
| naval | service | Ottawa |
| Please | dont | object |

Please read the conditions on back and sign your name and address thereon for reference.

*Harry's telegram to his father requesting permission to learn to fly, as he was under 21 years of age.*

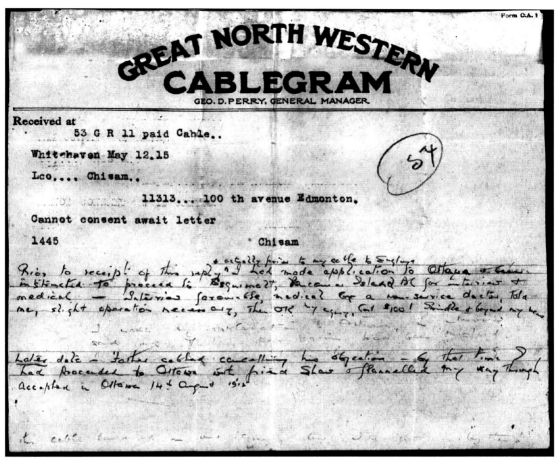

This telegram was from Harry's father refusing permission for Harry to learn to fly, and with Harry's comments underneath.

"Prior to receipt of this reply & actually prior to my cable to England I had made application to Ottawa and been instructed to proceed to Esouimalt, Vancouver Island, B.C. for interview & medical – Interview favourable and medical by a non-service doctor. Told me, slight operation necessary, then OK. My surgery cost $100! Swindle and beyond my means.
I made an appointment in Ottawa and in interview said to me the insistence on the operation had been mistaken.
Later date: Father cabled cancelling his objection – by this time I had proceeded to Ottawa with friend Shaw and flanelled my way through. Accepted in Ottawa on 14th August 1915."

# TRAINING AGREEMENT

Date _Oct 4 1915_

The **Wright Company** agrees to give _____

_Wm H Chisam_

lessons in flying under the following conditions :

    _First:_—The signing of the release of responsibility appended hereto.

                  Two hundred and fifty dollars ($250.00)
    _Second:_—The payment of $25.00 (Twenty-five dollars) per lesson, terms cash in advance unless otherwise arranged with our representative, which entitles the pupil to a total of four (4) hours of training flights.

    _Third:_—A lesson shall consist of one flight of fifteen minutes or more duration at the option of the instructor. The company does not agree to train a pupil to fly in any definite number of flights, nor does it assume any responsibility beyond the breakage of the machine during the training. The pupil, therefore, can take as many lessons as he may in his own judgment deem necessary.

    _Fourth:_—A record shall be kept of each lesson furnished with the pupil's acknowledgment.

THE WRIGHT COMPANY,

Per _Orville Wright_

Witness : _M. Beck_

    _Acceptance:_—I hereby accept the above conditions for taking lessons to fly the Wright aeroplane.

    In taking these lessons with __the appointed__ Operator I do so of my own volition and hereby assume whatever risk of personal injury there may be connected with it. I agree for myself and my heirs not to hold __the appointed__ Operator, or The Wright Company, either individually or collectively, liable for any injury which I may sustain from these flights.

_W. H. Chisam_

Witness : _M. Beck_

_Training Agreement, signed by Orvill Wright. Harry went to Dayton on 2nd October 1915._

34

*Flight Lieutenant Chisam in casual stance with propellor.*

*Harry. Dayton Ohio in 1915.*

*Ally Shaw, Dayton Ohio in 1915.*

*Fellow trainee pilots in Dayton, Ohio, USA, in 1915.*

**Biplane with Harry and his instructor.**

*Wright Biplane*
*landing in 1915.*

*Wright School of Aviation,*
*Dayton, Ohio, USA, 1915.*
*Harry is second from right.*

*Harry and Ally in Dayton, Ohio, 1915.*

*Memorial at Dayton Ohio. Harry's name is four rows from the bottom, and fourth from right.*

*Algonquin Grill in
Dayton, Ohio.*

*Moving the flying school
to the railroad depot.*

*Re-assembling aircraft
and tented hangars at
Augusta, Georgia.*

*School machines and hangars at the Wright School
of Aviation, Augusta, Georgia. December 1915.*

*Qualifying for pilot's licence.
5 January 1916.*

*Harry's American flying
licence, No. 385.*

20th September, Wilbur had flown in a complete circle, staying in the air 90 seconds. In all they trained 116 pilots at Huffman Prairie whose names, Harry Chisam's among them, are recorded on a plaque.

Training was largely dependent on the weather and took time. The agreement signed entitled the bearer to just four hours in the air. On this they would be judged proficient – or not – to receive the Federation Aeronautique Internationale Aero Club of America certificate. The licence Harry Chisam received was number 385. There were really very few pilots in the world at the start of the Great War and luckily for Britain, Harry Chisam was one of them. However now, he thought gloomily, his chances of making it to Europe that year looked bleaker than ever.

Just then the door to the Algonquin Grill opened and two instructors accompanied Orville Wright into the centre of the room.

"I know a whole bunch of you are feeling pretty low because of the weather. We have no option, we can't fly in this and I know Ohio, this is the way of it and we'll not be flying here again this year. Not here. I can't stop long. I have to go down the railroad depot and make arrangements. I want to add there'll be no additional cost to your training." Wright had their complete attention now. Other diners paused out of respect for the man, America's pioneer of aviation. Robertson carefully replaced the coffee pot. It didn't look like Mr Wright was going to be staying on for coffee.

"What we are going to do is transfer the school south. It'll mean a lot of extra work. You'll have to help us unbolt the aeroplanes and the hangars and all the equipment. We'll have to take it all down. Then we'll have to load it on railroad cars. It's a lot of work. Can I count on you?"

Everyone nodded. Harry Chisam suddenly jumped up, "We'll do everything we can to help. We simply must have those aero certificates."

Wright nodded. "I know. OK I want you all to meet me back at Huffman at 12 noon."

"Where are we going to, sir," said Ally Shaw.

"Augusta. Augusta, Georgia." Abruptly Wright turned on his heel and with a polite nod to Robertson marched out of the restaurant.

"Where the Sam Bell is Georgia?" asked Ally Shaw.

Robertson poured out more coffee. "It's way down south, sir, one of the original thirteen colonies to rebel. Thought you'd have known that, you all being British."

The dismantling of the school continued day and night. The aeroplanes were taken apart too. A special train was held in a siding at Dayton depot and railroad staff rallied round as the young men with strange accents unloaded wagon loads of spars and wheels and cabling. In all 34 British and Canadian flyers qualified at Wright's flying school that winter and would go on to fly in France. Then one afternoon the locomotive was backed hissing and steaming on to the train. Several townspeople came to see off the school, among them several excitable girls who hitched their horses to the rail outside the telegraph office and jumped up and down. Robertson walked down from the restaurant just in time to see the train pulling slowly out on to the main line. People lined the track waving, but Robertson stood on a little hummock and as the train went by he saw Harry Chisam on the platform at the back of the rearmost car. The Englishman waved and smiled genially. Robertson raised his hand in farewell, feeling suddenly tired and old. His normal, smiling, good humour deserted him. The road to freedom he knew was long and bloody. He trudged back to the Algonquin Grill, knowing it would echo ever after with the laughter of brave young men about to set off for war.

# In God We Trust

"The President will see you now, Mr Chisam."

Flicking a hand back through his hair Harry Chisam followed the aide de camp through the doors into the Oval Office, bigger than he had imagined. At the side of the room a man was straightening papers on a table.

"Mr President? William Hargrove Chisam."

The elder man straightened up and turned to Harry Chisam.

"Mr Chisam, good of you to drop by."

"Mr President, it's an honour to meet you."

"Oh no, young man, the honour is all mine, you're off to join the new war," said Woodrow Wilson. Then he looked shrewdly at the young man in a tweed suit before him. "Think you'll win?"

"Yes sir, we'll win. There is absolutely no doubt about that whatsoever."

Wilson turned to his desk in the centre of the room. The young man before him oozed ebullience and confidence, such a contrast to the German ambassador, haughtily threatening Wilson with attacks on Atlantic shipping.

"Your grandfather was a Methodist preacher at Annetwell Street chapel in Carlisle, so was mine."

"Yes, sir."

"Our peoples are very similar, aren't they?" Wilson said.

"Americans are more fun," Chisam blurted out, remembering a string of girlfriends in Ohio and Georgia. Wilson laughed. "Well I don't know about that. I guess I forget about that on my side of the desk. When do you sail?"

"Tomorrow from New York – there's a whole group of us, several of us trained here in the United States. We came down from Canada."

"We're glad we could help out," said Wilson dryly. "What will you do when you get to England?"

"Now I have my pilot's licence I can start air training straight away – I'll be sent up to Redcar in Yorkshire. Then it will be coastal work, I think, although I don't know."

"Coastal work? What does that entail?"

"We're using aeroplanes to spot enemy shipping. But now with better guns mounted we can actually search out U boats and sink 'em."

"That certainly sounds good for us. The Germans have been very contrary."

American shipping was the next target for U-boat warfare.

The servant had reappeared and coughed politely.

Harry Chisam, taking his cue, bade farewell.

"I'll make sure we stop them, sir."

"Why thank you, thank you," and he slapped a sheaf of papers into his hand repeatedly.

"Mr Chisam? What makes you so sure you can win – I mean the Austrian empire, Germany, even the Turks, lined up against you? Hell of a job."

"Got a dollar bill on you, sir?"

Wilson looked puzzled. "I'm not sure I have."

"Here take a dekko at one of mine."

Wilson looked at the greenback and then up at Chisam smiling cheerily in the centre of the massive room, the winter sun streaming down though the high windows.

"Just read what it says, sir, after the guff about promising to pay."

The servant coughed again and took Harry Chisam by the elbow.

"Goodbye sir, thank you very much, sir."

As the doors closed behind Harry Chisam, President Wilson read again the inscription all US dollar bills carry. It would be many months before America entered the war, but President Wilson set about building the foundations of American involvement early in January 1916. Would they win or not? He could only repeat Harry Chisam's message, "In God We Trust."

There is a legend that Woodrow Wilson once told his friends he went to war because he owed a British naval officer a dollar bill. No one really believed him, but in any event they both won the war.

*"Americans are more fun." Harry and Jean met in Ohio.*

# Training in the North

"Let's get everyone up on deck for a photo," said Raymond Collishaw. The wind blew fiercely as they stood in a line, ten newly-qualified naval pilots sailing for England. "Make it quick, Colly," said Lloyd Breadner, "Wouldn't do if we were lost at sea." And everyone laughed as the ship's photographer took their picture.

Harry Chisam sailed for Britain aboard the White Star liner, the Adriatica, on 12th January 1916. Among his ten shipmates were Ally Shaw and Raymond Collishaw who would go on to be Air Vice Marshall and was Harry Chisam's commanding officer at Naval Three squadron in France. Chisam almost crashed on his qualifying flight in Augusta. The piston rod on his Wright B snapped and pushed its way out of the cylinder block. This happened in mid air but Harry Chisam steadily nursed the plane down and landed safely.

"Kind of an advantage, having gotten down like that," said his instructor, pushing back his cap. "Reckon you'll be able to land even when you've been shot up by enemy gunfire."

"I'm very grateful," said Harry. The instructor, a weather beaten man, spat on the ground.

Chisam with Shaw, Collishaw and three others duly presented themselves at RNAS Redcar on 3rd February 1916.

"What do you think of the station commander?" said Harry.

"Well, I'm not sure, bit of a wag really."

"Oh, what makes you say that?" He and Ally were walking back to their lodgings in the village. The airfield was half a mile away from the village where the fledgling pilots were billeted. The officers walked to and from the aerodrome four times a day. Their feet pressed down through the soft snow.

"I went in with Ray Collishaw and we introduced ourselves. I said I preferred to be known as Ally Shaw. The man looked from Ray to me and back again and he says, "Ah the two Shaws – Colly Shaw and Ally Shaw.""

Harry put his weight on a frozen puddle watching the ice splinter and fracture along a dozen seams.

"Really? Are you absolutely sure?"

"Positive ... Oh do shut up Chisam!"

The following day the newcomers took to the air flying with instructors in dual controlled G.3 Caudrons. The plane was different from the Wright brothers' machines. However it was almost as primitive. Sitting in the cockpit the pilot held between his legs the joystick which steered the craft. Pull it back and the aircraft went up, forward and it dived, left and the wing warped turning it left. The rudder bar on the floor at the pilot's feet worked the tail turning left or right. No aeroplane will fly in a straight line; it veers left or right, up and down. The skill lies in minutely adjusting the passage of the craft. Novice pilots tended to over-compensate. Training accidents were frequent. Germany alone lost 18,000 pilots throughout the war in training accidents.

Snow and fog stopped flying at Redcar early in February. The weather in the first half of that year was atrocious. It would be June before the pilots notched up sufficient solo flying hours to qualify.

Pilots trained on a variety of aircraft and training was very thorough. These included the Caudron G.3 , the Avro 504c, Grahame-White Type XV and the Curtiss JN-4.

Pupils were taught to roll, spin, loop and the climbing turn called the chandelle.

As well as actual flying, all pilots spent considerable time taking the aircraft apart, understanding thoroughly how the craft worked and fitted together. Pilots were expected to be able to effect repairs on downed aircraft. In theory if not in practice each could dismantle and rebuild his plane. Then it was back to the classroom as the theories of aerodynamics were spelled out. Pilots also studied geography and navigation.

After he had recovered from his crash, Harry Chisam graduated from Redcar. The aircraft had crashed several times and was now broken up. Harry proceeded to the Royal Naval Air Service training established at Cranwell. New fliers were taught how

to shoot moving targets from a moving aircraft. Ingenious engineers set up a gun turret on a small railway. The pilot would cannon along the track blasting away at a lineside target.

"What the hell did you miss it for?" the military instructor bawled at Chisam.

"I think I was distracted sergeant."

"Well get un-distracted, sir, get back on target. The enemy he don't get distracted, he'll shoot your bloody balls off, distracted or not. Try it again."

Even though it was bitterly cold they blasted away until dusk.

Later the instructor looked out of the window of the sergeants' mess. Two figures were stealing across the meadow from the shooting range. A brace of rabbits dangled from their belts. Yet they carried no rifles.

"Distracted, my bloody Aunt Sally," the sergeant grumbled but decided to say no more about it.

Harry Chisam received his pilot's certificate on 6 September 1916 at what is now RAF Cranwell, the air force college of flying.

*Killingholme, February 1916.*

*Qualified pilots on way back to UK
from New York to Liverpool in
January 1916 on the 'Adriatic'.*

*Avro 504C
(long
range).*

*French
Caudron
with 80HP
Gnome
Engine.*

*Curtiss Jenny.*

*Harry in a Graham White Box Kite.*

"Have another kipper dear."

Harry Chisam manfully addressed the seconds knowing any refusal would be ill-received.

"And eggs, dear boy, have some more poached eggs. Elsie have you more eggs?"

"Really father."

"You need eggs, m'boy. Boxers train on eggs."

"Boxing? They've said I can have a gun, Dad."

Between July and September 1916 Harry Chisam was stationed in Scotland at a Royal Naval air station in east Lothian at East Fortune.

"I tell you it's called East Fortune," he said as he and Ally Shaw tried to find the town on a map spread across the table in the mess at Redcar.

"Well, I suppose you've already gone west young man, so perhaps it's as well to go east, seek your fortune, what?"

# Heart of Midlothian

The late September sun sparkled on the seas as the aircraft, a lone Avro 504, droned in low over the old wooden rowing boat.

"What do we do, grandfather? He's seen us!" the boy shouted.

The old man pulled on the oars, "Start waving, son. Wave for all your worth. If he thinks we're a U-boat we're done for." As he bent to the oars old Mac pondered the poetry of dying on the firth of Forth setting kreels with his grandson, while his own boy was so far away. Even now would his son be trudging across the newly harvested fields of northern France?

The aircraft screamed in very low, just a few feet above the waves, dancing in the setting sun.

"I turned back and came in with the sun behind me," Harry Chisam said later. "I couldn't see the craft clearly and I wanted a closer look. But it was no good; I could hardly see him."

"You realise that would have given the U-boat time to dive."

"Yes I know, but I wanted to test my guns – they jammed yesterday."

Chisam let lose a fierce burst of fire as he edged round to begin his approach.

The boy, barely six years old, stood in the boat waving but he was just a speck on the sun dappled water, a shadow that had caught the hunter's eye.

"Well that'll be all I suppose," said the CO shuffling up his papers. "Look, don't worry about it, we have to face these things. Come on, the adjutant and I are running out to North Berwick for a drink."

Even for a Saturday the harbour-side pub was quiet. Four elderly men sat around a table drinking beer, one with a lavish white beard rested his chin on a walking stick. For all of them it was a sombre moment. The attack on the fishing boat had brought home to all of them the nearness of the war. "Even the football team has joined up," one of them said.

"Do you think they'll ever play here again?"

"They cannae play anyway."

The three men looked expectantly at the man with the white beard.

"Wee Davey all right, now?"

Just then the door opened and three naval officers walked in. "I'll get these, chief," said a tall, rather dark man. He looked tired and leant heavily on the bar.

The landlord appeared and the officer ordered large whiskies.

"Och, Wee Davey's all right. Thinks it's a hoot, so he does." The man shook his head from side to side. "Came right out of the sun he did, just like the story books say. I could hardly see him. But Davey jumped up and down waving my old scarf. Then I heard the guns firing – just a brief burst. So I pulled the boat shorewards, veering away. My word, he was low, I swear his wheels skimmed the very tops of the waves. I believe he'd hae hit us anyway even if he didnae fire."

"Like as not he wanted to get a good look at you."

The old man's friends made him go through the story and again and again. The extra quick pull back to shore and the aircraft suddenly banking steeply away as if to put distance between the awful tragedy that might have been. Wee Davey jumping up and down, how brave!

"Good night gentlemen," the landlord said as the officers stood up and made for the door. In the commotion Harry Chisam beckoned him to the end of the bar. Later when the car roared away outside the landlord carried four large whiskies across to the table.

Harry Chisam was flying an Avro 504 from East Fortune. Much of the work was patrolling the steel grey waters of the Forth. In the car the Adjutant said, "We lost a warship here, the HMS Pathfinder, back in '14. Torpedoed by a U-boat, 500 men killed. We must make sure that never happens again."

"How did the Germans know where to send the sub?"

"Good question." The adjutant changed gear. "They had a spy, a man called Lody, Carl Hans Lody. He had been watching our fleet and telegraphing information to his controller in Stockholm. The police caught him, he was charged with treason and hung in the Tower."

"I remember the trial. Hadn't he been in America?"

"He'd been married to an American and spoke English fluently."

"I believe he was caught wearing a German overcoat."

The adjutant nodded, "I think they worked out a method of intercepting his messages and the Berlin label on his coat rather proved the case."

"Whit's this Bill?"

"Frae the gentlemen, I don't know why."

The men supped the whisky appreciatively.

"Good lads these naval officers eh?"

"Och you can always depend on the navy," said Mac.

# La Vie en France

Early in December 1916 Harry Chisam received transfer orders.
"France," he said waving the order sheet, jumping up from the piano, "I'm off to join No. 3 Wing in France."

"You take care over there. France indeed; don't know who's the greater danger, the women or the Hun."

"Really, that's quite unnecessary." Mrs Chisam said.

"I was well taught in the United States, Dad," said Harry. A warning look from his mother stopped him adding, "On both counts."

By the end of 1916 the armies had fought each other to a standstill. Neither fully understood the impact of the machine gun or the growing importance of aerial warfare. The Germans and the British and French faced each other across a tartan of hastily dug trenches that slashed the fields of Flanders and northern France all the way from the North Sea to the Swiss border. Cavalry was of no use against machine guns. Vast numbers of men would perish as the very nature of warfare changed from manual might to mechanised dexterity.

No. 3 Wing had been formed to serve in the ill-fated Dardanelles campaign. In the summer of 1916, it retrained as a long range bomber squadron. The war in the air was coming of age. Both sides could fire through the propeller and machines were becoming lighter and more manoeuvrable.

"I remember No. 3 Wing had trained hard and carried out audacious bombing raids over Mulheim, Oberndorf and the Thyssen steel works at Hagendingen, before I joined. More raids followed over Saarbrucken, Dillingen and Volklingen. The squadron was based at Luxueuil. The weather was bad in December when I arrived."

To compound the agony of the western front, heavy snow, rain and cold laid a rigor mortis across battlefield and lines. Troops died of cold and disease in the trenches. Pilots suffered frostbite, guns jammed and cabling snapped. Poor visibility kept the bombers grounded. Harry Chisam was in time for the last raid of the year to Dillingen on 27th December 1916. The strength of the German air service was increasing, making the bombing raids more impracticable. Further raids took place over Saarbrucken in January. However a decision had already been taken to transfer the pilots of No. 3 Wing across to the new naval combat squadrons being formed to fight on the western front. In December 1916 the Army Council had approved the expansion of the Royal Flying Corps to 106 active and 95 reserve squadrons. Two more were to be retained for night flying. However it was not enough. There was now considerable consternation on the part of the allied commanders as to the ultimate outcome of the war. Germany declared unrestricted submarine warfare in the Atlantic. The Russians were crumbling before the might of the German army. The Italians, allied with the French and British, suffered heavy reverses.

---

"What do you mean, they're retreating?"

"Only what I have heard," said Harry Chisam. "Bloke in the office has seen the aerial reconnaissance photos; the Germans are falling back."

In fact, starting in February 1917 allied aircraft picked up pictures of German troops falling back to a straighter better defended system of fortifications, which became known as the Hindenburg line. The countryside so recently vacated was burnt and buildings blown up, a scorched earth policy that torched the frozen landscape and made it all but impassable. The line stretched a hundred miles from Lens near Arras to Aisne near Soissons. It effectively straightened the German front line and was, in the opinion of the German High Command, utterly impregnable. The men of the Royal Naval Air Service and the Royal Flying Corps disagreed.

In contrast to the horrors of mud and explosion that daily threatened and then ended the lives of thousands it is worth recording the lighter side of a pilot's life, at least behind the lines. RNAS pilots, like their brothers-in-arms in the RFC, flew hard and played hard. The mess rooms and quarters, often quickly dismantled and re-erected, were nevertheless comfortable places. In a world without running water and electricity, ground staff performed near miracles of ingenuity to look after the squadrons. Pilots dined well and would travel into Paris and Nancy to relax. Boisterous parties ensued.

One night at the Grand Hotel in Nancy officers from the French air force, Groupe de Bombardment, under the charismatic General Happe, a cadre of Chasseurs Alpins and RNAS No. 3 wing, met for dinner. It turned in to a noisy party with wine and champagne flowing. Suddenly the local French military commandant – who had authority over all military personnel in the area – strode into the restaurant. Lampshades swung from the ceiling, a bevy of chorus girls scuttled out through the kitchens. Harry Chisam loked up from the piano as silence fell and the French officers realised they could be in deep trouble.

However the RNAS knew nothing of this or who he was. Cheering wildly two Canadian air men picked the man up and sat him on their shoulders. He was carried through the ranks of the air forces and placed on a table. Harry Chisam had the presence of mind to thrust a full glass of cognac into his hand. The commandant looked round severely. Then he raised his glass and said, "Vive la France et vive L'Angleterre," drank off his brandy and bade the company good luck. Everyone stood to attention as Harry gave his first public rendition of *La Marseillaise*.

The German troops started withdrawing in February 1917. The RFC and RNAS stepped up patrols. Fighting in the skies above Arras and over the River Somme was intense.

Harry Chisam transferred for two weeks to a training squadron, No. 11, but was pulled off and reassigned to No. 1 squadron based at La Bellevue – near Arras, in April 1917, flying Sopwith Triplanes. Naval squadrons 1, 8 and 10 were equipped with the planes affectionately known as tripehounds or tripes.

*No. 1 Naval Squadron snowbound at La Bellevue aerodrome.*

*No. 3 Naval Squadron.*

# The Battle of Arras

The weather continued cold and wet. Rifles froze solid and flying was limited by fog and ice. The Germans stepped up air activity as their troops fell back to the Hindenburg line. In an effort to break the deadlock the French and British decided to attack the German front line in the spring. Robert Nivelle, the new commander of the French armies, would mount an offensive in the region of the Aisne river. As a diversion and to weaken the enemy further, the British were to attack north of Arras. More aircraft than ever were needed for aerial reconnaissance, observing and photographing enemy troops. The pictures could be developed, expanded and would then give the analysts back behind the lines far more information than a flying observer could pick up. Work of this sort, which had started with air balloons, grew increasingly important as the war progressed. Fighter pilots, like Harry Chisam, had to accompany the reconnaissance machines, shadowing them across enemy lines, clearing the skies ahead and then shepherding them back. The second major task was to range artillery. Aircraft would fly over the enemy, observing where the shells landed and then radioing back to base (via a primitive wireless transmitter using Morse code) how far short or over the bombs were falling. The German air service valiantly disrupted this, fighting spirited actions against the French and British. Legends were born on both sides.

However, The Royal Flying Corps lost many men and machines. A certain desperation is evident at the start of 1917.

"You are asking me to fight the battle this year (1917) with the same machines I fought it with last year. We shall be hopelessly outclassed," said Hugh Trenchard, the head of the Royal Flying Corps. To help Trenchard – pilots called him Boom Trenchard – several Royal Naval Air Service squadrons were formed and put at his disposal in the region of Arras. Much of Harry Chisam's work that spring with Naval One squadron was flying escort to aerial reconnaissance teams. The weather continued cold. Snow fell on La Bellevue aerodrome. The allied air offensive over Arras and a comprehensive artillery bombardment started on 4th April 1917. Five days later ground troops threw themselves at German positions. The carnage was horrific. Men walked calmly out of their trenches and across no-man's land to be mown down continuously by machine gun fire. 10th April saw a snow storm along the front and on the following day it snowed again. Aircraft cockpits were open then and pilots had to fight cold and numbness. Troops on the front itself could in some instances not fire their rifles because of the cold. The battle raged until 16th May 1917. The hoped-for breakthrough failed. Although Canadian troops took Vimy Ridge north of Arras, the French offensive in the south made little headway. Morale among French troops all but collapsed. Thousands died. So many were the casualties that stretcher parties couldn't cope. Many wounded men simply froze to death on the ground where they fell. Mutiny was rife. Nivelle was replaced by Petain.

For the men of the RFC and RNAS there was a further hazard. The German air service was now re-equipping with the Alabatros DIII, more manoeuvrable and stronger than their counterparts. Moreover the legendary Red Baron, Manfred von Richthofen, was flying at the head of a crack squadron from Douai directly opposite Arras.

The lone aircraft climbed high to escape the clouds at 2,000 feet. It had been madness to go up, but Harry Chisam flew on undaunted. With the afternoon sun in front of him he was headed for home and low on fuel after a lengthy detour behind enemy lines. Suddenly glancing in the mirror he'd fitted he saw a speck in the sky moving far too fast. Immediately he flew into a curve and drawing the joystick back gained height, knowing that as he did so his air speed would slow. The speck became an enemy aircraft (EA) coming straight towards him. Calmly he flexed his hands and breathed deeply. Numb with cold he could hardly feel the controls, but by now a certain instinct born of long hours flying over the North Sea and France guided him. The Tripehound shuddered and climbed. It reminded him of a fox hound he'd once seen jumping and then belly flopping over a five-bar gate outside Hawkshead. The enemy had disappeared but was no longer coming straight at him. Without really knowing why, Chisam turned and flew back, the sun behind him. Suddenly out of the clouds to his left shot a red aircraft, a triplane, looping the loop, upside down, screaming for traction against the very sky. Too late, he knew he could never expect to hit him. The enemy aircraft came screaming in at right angles to his plane. But nothing happened and the EA turned again. Harry could swear afterwards he heard the click – the EA's guns had jammed. What he wasn't prepared for was the actions of the pilot. Flying almost upside down over the top of his Tripehound the German waved cheerily, pointed at his now useless guns and flew on. Chisam turned for home. Only later did he realise who it was.

"He seemed really quite friendly," he remarked.

"He'll have you next time, Harry. They don't call him the Bloody Red Baron for nothing you know."

By 16th May the offensive had ground to a standstill. However, hostilities in the air continued. On 13th June German Gothas bombed London, occasioning near-panic in parliament. "It does politicians good to be bombed occasionally," remarked Trenchard acidly. The average life expectancy for a pilot on the western front was now just 18 hours in the air. Part of this appalling casualty rate was the lack of experience of new pilots. Many arrived fresh from England and took to the air never to return. Their bags still stood unpacked by their beds. German pilots were crossing the lines more often and were much in evidence. The 1st Field Survey Company, Royal Engineers, was in charge of aerial observation. For best results, everyone understood, aircraft had to drone in low and slow over the German lines. The arrival of the Red Baron and the Flying Circus made it more dangerous than ever.

One German infantry officer later wrote, "During these days, there was a whole series of dogfights, which almost invariably ended in defeat for the British since it was Richthofen's squadron they were up against. Often five or six planes in succession would be chased away or shot down in flames."

# Belgium and the Sea

"Let's see then, I've never been that high before," said Tich Rochford, surveying the new fighter planes drawn up on the grass. Mechanics had the engine cowlings up. Naval Three squadron was being re-equipped with Sopwith Camels.

"The greatest problem at that height is oxygen," said Harry Chisam. "The canisters and equipment are too heavy to fit. Lack of oxygen will make you feel tired and sluggish."

"I feel like that anyway." Everyone laughed. Chisam had been ferrying the new aircraft over the Channel and was enthusiastic about them.

"OK. Let's do it now." The flight took off and climbed slowly, circling round and round until it reached 22,000 feet. It was the highest any of them had flown. Far below snaked the French coastline. The pilots could see right across Kent and beyond into East Anglia; far away in the west they could make out Dorset. After a few minutes Rochford started diving, careful not to stall, curving ever downwards like a sycamore leaf. Looking back into France and Belgium, the miles of mud and flooded farm land that was to become Passchendaele glinted in the afternoon sun. Much of Flanders was reclaimed marsh land. Despite the best efforts of farmers locally, between the opposing armies, water welled back across the meadows making a quagmire for a battlefield.

Harry Chisam joined Naval Three in July at Furnes near Dunkerque. Naval Three had been transferred there after the battles over the Somme and Arras that spring. He arrived with a delivery of new Sopwith Camels on 13th July and flew his first patrol the following afternoon, setting out across the North Sea at 5.45pm. Much of the work of Naval Three was patrolling the coast, protecting the fleet as it ferried troops and munitions back and forth across the Channel.

The failure of the Aisne offensive further south persuaded the British under Douglas Haig to try a further push up the Flemish coast to retake Ostende and Zeebrugge. Royal Naval pilots had tried to bomb the submarine pens on the Belgian coast without success. Unrestricted submarine warfare was slowly wresting control of the seas. America had entered the war on 6th April 1917. That month alone the German U-boats had sunk 881,027 gross tons of shipping. For the Americans to join the war they had first to get across the Atlantic.

"It's not simply the Atlantic," Harry Chisam remarked in the mess one night, "We've got to get them across the Channel after that."

"I wonder who they'll send; I mean what their soldiers are like," an English RFC officer said.

"You trained there, Chisam, what do you think?"

"Like Canadians, outdoors, tough, hardy – Wright was backing us – took us down to Georgia to finish our training when the bad weather set in."

"Yes, but it's one thing taking on the Sioux Indians and the Mexicans. I mean who do you think they'll send? The Hole in the Wall gang?"

"I don't know," said Chisam.

"Can they fight? Are they energetic enough, enervated as the French would say?"

Chisam thought back to his own experiences in the United States and the name of a girl that adorned his plane.

"Oh they're energetic enough," he said and smiled equably.

"Delivering that last Camel was difficult though. We need more if we're to protect the Channel."

"It's not just the Channel," said the adjutant moodily, "The bombers are getting through."

"We know they can make love," said Ally Shaw later, "Question is old son, can they make war?!"

Late one July afternoon Harry Chisam was returning from patrol over the North Sea. He flew with B flight under Jim Glen. Many of these patrols were quiet affairs with no enemy aircraft in sight. Fleet protection meant driving off German aircraft and making sure the troopships criss-crossing the Channel could do so without mishap. RNAS aeroplanes routinely climbed to 15,000 feet and then flew large sweeps across the sky searching for enemy aircraft below. The aircraft flew circles encompassing the ships and the shore, gradually losing height until time and low fuel bade them return home. Communication between pilots was almost non existent – there was no radio, hand signals were all they had. Harry Chisam flew on, constantly alert, scanning the sky in a circular motion of the neck that wore out silk scarfs – gifts from girls now so far away.

Jim Glen had led the flight up to 15,000 feet and 15 miles out from Ostende. Now heading south west with the sun pretty much in front of them they were attacked from behind. Harry Chisam saw the aircraft in front of him dive suddenly and instinctively threw his Camel into a roll. Turning his head right he saw four Albatros scouts diving from 15,000 feet straight at them. The setting sun and the end of the patrol – it was 6.30pm – gave them the element of surprise. He kicked the rudder bar hard, pushing the joystick forward, not too suddenly, but firmly. "Bob like a duck, old girl," he whispered. But it was too late – a stream of bullets scattered in the plane and to his surprise he saw them march and stutter across the instruments directly in front of him. Instinctively he levelled out of the dive as the Albatros swept underneath him. From his left he saw Jim Glen rolling in to help. Glen flushed another Albatros off his tail and guns blazing drove him down very quickly. The enemy aircraft crashed into the sea. Chisam saw his attacker starting to climb several hundred feet ahead of him. Powering up he eased the joystick back intending to climb and cross the German's trajectory further up. The German was flying directly in front of the sun; Chisam knew he'd fire blind if the aircraft was lit up. It was worth a try. Then to his horror he realised the aircraft was not responding to his controls, the nose wouldn't come up. Not only would he miss the shot he'd worked out but the EA would turn on him and finish him off. He knew the Camel would still be able to dive whatever had happened to the engine. Best fly on straight ahead. The Albatros was growing smaller, dwindling away in the distance. Chisam looked quickly around but the other members of B flight had chased off. Then he saw Glen circling over head. He had guessed what had happened and was guarding his friend. Harry was down below 2,000 feet now and could see the waves rolling up Coxyde beach. It was around seven o'clock and the tide was out. He realised the engine had been hit and the controls were damaged but he was still able to turn and fly the aircraft. The engine held up well and he flew along the beach checking the rushing sands below.

"Oh dear, here we go again," he thought. An old man was walking his dog. "I just hope you have the sense to move inland old cock," thought Harry Chisam.

He flew back up the beach facing the way he'd come, noting the wind and

*Sopwith Camels.*

*Harry named a number of aircraft
after girlfriends in the United States.*

*Coming in to land.*

*Squadron in formation.*

*B. Flight of Sopwith Camels
ready for patrol.*

*Harry and Ally Shaw. Pilots kept
dogs for company and continuity.*

touched down lightly on the sands. Coming to a standstill he cut the engine and climbed out of the cockpit. The old man panted up looking at the bullet holes in the wings. The dog was yapping furiously and wagging its stubby tail.

"Cette guerre, déjà, cette une chose dangereuse, n'est ce pas?" the man said.

Harry Chisam bent down to pat the dog on his head. His hands were shaking and he didn't want the Frenchman to see this.

"There's a good boy," he said, "There's a good old boy."

"Il aime bien entendre l'anglais, lui," the old man laughed and suddenly he and Harry Chisam shook hands. Whatever people might say in the years ahead, Harry Chisam always maintained the French were damn good people to have on your side in a war.

———— •─•─ ————

CPO Finch shook his head reluctantly as he and Harry Chisam examined the plane where he'd landed on the beach. B3794 'Aline II' was badly shot up.

"Lucky to get out of this all right, sir," said a rating poking about inside the cockpit.

Harry Chisam scribbled a list of what had happened. "Is it the left longeron?" This is the main brace of the aircraft running from front to rear.

"Yes – top left," the rating shouted back.

Top left longeron shot through twice, badly splintered, Harry wrote. Seat rail shot away by explosive bullet missing petrol tank by inches. Petrol tank bearer fractured. Main plane spar connections shot through, locking box buckled. Right hand strut, rear of pilot's seat, shot through. Front engine bearer shot through – five holes. Chisam looked up. A lorry was making its way up the beach to carry the stricken aircraft home. It would be dark soon. Left diagonal engine strut badly splintered.

The rating called out, "Bottom elevator shot through – no wonder you couldn't climb, sir, you were lucky to be left with any control at all."

Harry Chisam looked up the beach at the waves rolling in and carried on writing it all down. Putting it on paper it didn't read like a narrow escape from death.

"Right, let's have a look at the wings," said the rating. Not for the first time Chisam sent up a silent prayer of thanks for the ground crew. They were excellent men. He knew they'd go over the plane until they found every single fault and then and only then would a decision be taken as to whether to scrap Aline II or repair her. There was no question of short cuts.

Bottom wings, Harry wrote.

"The control of the bottom wings is shot away," said Smith, working his way along the wings that so recently had defied gravity.

Bottom right plane, main spar hit, one rib and socket shot through. Bottom left plane front spur holed. Bottom right aileron main spar shot through. Rudder and fin pierced about six times.

Harry Chisam stood on a pair of ladders and placed his fingers in the holes the bullets had made in the tail. Sometimes they were so close together it was impossible to estimate how many had passed through.

Back at the aerodrome Red Mulock said, "Lucky escape there, Harry. Very competent piece of flying; putting her down like that on the beach with virtually no control of the machine."

"Oh she knew the way home, sir."

"Yes well, I'm sending you over to England tomorrow to pick up a replacement. So you'll have to pay attention." Then he clapped Chisam on the back. "It'll be an easy trip, Harry. Well done."

---

One evening a few days later C flight landed. Jim Glen, the flight leader realised one of them had not returned. They had lost Skimp Abbott, a tall wiry Canadian trapper from the Yukon. Dismayed the men trudged back to the mess. No one had seen him and the patrol had been uneventful.

Later Tich Rochford appeared in the mess grinning broadly.

"Any news of the Abbott?" Jim Glen asked, looking over the top of a French newspaper.

"He got down all right on a beach I believe," said Rochford. "Probably skinning a rabbit or two in the dunes as we speak."

Just as the dinner gong sounded the door opened and Skimp Abbott ambled in. "Sorry I'm late, sir, I had to come back with engine trouble. When I took off again later, I couldn't find my patrol."

There was more to it than that. Flying at 10,000 feet above Nieuport, Abbott was attacked by three enemy aircraft.

"I thought maybe they were the rest of my flight," he said. The Germans realised this and let him get close before turning on him and attacking. Enemy fire blew the cowling off his engine, damaging the propeller.

Skimp Abbott went into a nose dive but regained control as he skimmed over the waves. Nursing his machine he glided in to make a forced landing on Coxyde beach.

"Chap with the terrier helped me out of the plane."

"Oh him, he's a good sort isn't he," Harry Chisam remarked.

---

"Mulock wants to see all of us after the funeral. What have you got there?"

"It's a wreath."

"I can see that, Harry," Tich Rochford said, "Who's it from."

"It's from a girl, I think she's an actress. Kathryn Martyn."

"Kathryn, yes, very pretty girl. She and Casey were engaged." The two airmen walked across the green grass of the cemetery. So many of the graves were new, the fresh earth mounded up in neat rows, boxed off and exactly parallel in this their final parade.

Francis Casey had returned from leave in England on 10th August. The next morning immediately after breakfast he flew off in his Camel re-familiarising himself with being in the air. Casey rolled and soared and dived. Putting his aircraft into a spin Casey hammered down towards the ground realising too late he had left far too little time to pull out. Seriously injured he was taken to hospital in La Panne where he died that afternoon. The funeral took place that evening when the patrols were over for the day. Red Mulock, the squadron leader, was a good friend of Francis Casey. In a calm voice he went through the precautions they should all take for safe flying: gain height, don't take unnecessary risks, don't show off. The pilots were young, full of fun and Mulock realised this as he travelled back with the priest to Dunkerque.

In London that night Kathryn Martyn took the stage. Every smile for ever afterwards, she thought, would be a piece of acting. The show must go on. Her lover, Francis, had taken her smile with him to the grave.

"Get in the air as quick as you can," Lloyd Breadner shouted as he sprinted past the makeshift Armstrong huts where B flight slept. "If we hurry we'll get him."

"Do it now," murmured Harry Chisam rolling swiftly out of bed.

He and Harry Chisam were airborne at 06.10 on 18th August, pushing their machines as high as they could above Nieuport heading for Middelkerke. During that summer Naval Three had one flight on constant standby, able to scramble and take to the air in response to a telephoned alert of an enemy aircraft sighting. It was vital that the enemy be denied sight of troop movements as the battle of Ypres raged. Quite often the enemy aircraft would have disappeared or doubled back over the German lines. On a bright August morning Chisam saw the Albatros two-seater about a mile out to sea at 10,000 feet. He was 1,000 feet above the EA and coming straight out of the sun when he dived on the Albatros. The German observer spotted Chisam who started firing continuously. The EA dived in a bid to escape. Lloyd Breadner also tackled the enemy but on this occasion his guns jammed. Harry followed the Albatros down to 4,500 feet firing over 150 rounds. "I could see tracers entering the aircraft and the observer ceased firing. Either he was dead or his guns had jammed like Lloyd's," he said in the mess as he wolfed down scrambled eggs. "I didn't see it hit the drink, but he was in a bad way. I levelled out at 4,000 feet and headed out to sea, then home." Mindful of Mulock's warnings, he might have added.

"It's an absolute curse, guns jamming," Lloyd said, stamping around at the end of the room.

"Happened to me 30 miles north of Blankenberge – we were tackling those eight Gothas do you remember, on the 12th – the day after Casey bought it? Chased them all the way to Southend. One of them nearly crashed into the pier."

"Oh really Harry..."

"Anyway my guns seized completely. I couldn't clear them and came home."

Breadner took B flight up against seven Gotha bombers – heading towards England from Zeebrugge on the 22nd August. "You know I reckon if we hit them on the way back it would help," Harry said

"Hardly much help if they've already bombed London."

"Think about it, they're tired, probably low on fuel and ammunition. Moreover it'll make them think twice before setting out."

"It's an idea. I'll see it's passed on."

The weather that churned Passchendaele into mud stopped flying almost completely between 23rd August and 3rd September. Rain sheeted down, running in runnels down the hastily-built cart tracks on the airfield. Flying over the front line Harry Chisam could see the miles of mud and water. It had become a landscape without feature. No trees, no buildings, just the stench of decomposing flesh. At 200 feet pilots would make out the ribcage of dead horses, the motionless heap of two or three bodies round an exploded gun and the slender spears of burned trees. The shells that exploded created craters in the earth that quickly filled with rain water. The low lying Flanders fields could not drain away. More troubling still for many of the men of Naval Three was that the Canadian army had taken over this stretch of the front. 16,000 of them were to die between August and October 1917. Death came stuttering across the mud from machine guns hidden in concrete bunkers with five feet thick walls. The wounded died slowly, drowning in the mud. Men carried duck boards to walk upon but it was like fighting in quicksand. Over 1,000 Canadian bodies from the battle of Passchendaele were never recovered. The rain fell ceaselessly.

The pilots could play poker or read. Chisam, whatever the weather, liked to walk along the sea front at Coxyde. "I suppose you must know the beach there pretty well, old man," Lloyd Breadner said. They shook off their overcoats and stepped into a café.

"Shall we have a beer?"

The waiter approached, "Goedenavond," he said.

"Beer! Als'tu blieft."

For some while they sat in silence. Lloyd Breadner said, "I think I'll miss the beer and wine here when the war is over. What about you?"

"I won't miss anything about the war. Nothing."

"Will you go back to Canada?"

"I don't know. I doubt I'd settle in England – I like all this travel, and excitement. Perhaps I'll try gold panning in the Yukon – like the Abbott."

Breadner snorted. "Waste of time – the real money is in oil, laddie, mark my words. It's liquid gold."

"Oil? The black stuff that flies out of the engine when something goes wrong?"

"Think it through, our machines run on oil and petrol. Cars, ships and trains will be running on it soon. Get a stake in the oil business and you'll be a rich man."

"They haven't got any oil, in Canada."

The battles raged in Ypres as General Haig's plan of liberating the Belgium coast foundered in the mud of Passchendaele. Air combat continued through October. The weather closed in early and pilots reported guns frozen on 18th October.

---

"Well done Harry," remarked Lloyd Breadner, "That's your first official kill – I'm sure there are many more but we have to be careful what we can claim." Breadner reached down to poke the fire.

"Thank you, sir."

Tich Rochford joined them in the mess. The weather had changed and the sun was going down leaving a clear blue sky. The distant rumble of the guns fractured the quiet of a late summer's evening.

"Let's have a drink then, a toast to victory," Rochford said. "What happened?"

"We attacked four Albatros scouts just off Ostende. Harry got a good sight on one EA and fired a short burst into him. I saw the Hun carry on for a short distance and then dive. Harry had not time to watch him further to ascertain whether he was under control or not – but the sight on him was very good. Anyway twenty minutes later over Stelhilde we attacked four more Albatros scouts. Harry attacked one and saw his shots go into the machine just to the rear of the pilot's seat."

"I was quite close and I saw some of the shots plug into the pilot's back." Harry swilled the whisky round in his glass trying to understand the horror of it. The sight of the bullets zipping into the pilot and the head going forward hadn't seemed like a man dying at all.

"We had more enemy aircraft attacking us now. I saw Harry attack one more then you went into a spin – there were six Hun up above you wheeling round firing. I drew some of them but I saw four concentrate on Harry shooting him down to 50 feet."

"50 feet, I didn't realise I went that low."

"I really thought you were going to hit the deck but you pulled out in time and hedge-hopped home – you must have a crossed the lines back here a few seconds later." Breadner paused to sip his drink. He'd just finished writing the log. Outside in the summer's evening the mechanics were still seeing to their aircraft. It seemed absurd to imagine they had been fighting for their lives just a few minutes ago.

"Good hunting Harry," said Tich raising his glass.

Two days later the squadron moved to Bray Dunes, right on the coast and five miles west of Furnes just across the border in France.

"This is Farmer Dewitte on whose land we have positioned our aerodrome. The Dewittes are Flemish-speakers so there is no need to confuse them with your quite appalling French," Breadner told the men. The officers laughed and the farmer shook hands and stumped off.

"There we are then back under canvas on a good old farm," said Rochford looking around at the bell tents in which they were now to live.

*Under canvas again!*

"Owned by a man named twit," joked Harry.

Naval Three was to stay at Bray Dunes until being transferred back to England in November. The work continued escorting bombers up the coast to Ostende and Bruges, patrolling the seas, helping shepherd troop transports across and the constant duelling for air supremacy in the skies above the mud of Passchendaele.

---

In contrast to Harry Chisam's near death after being surrounded by enemy aircraft, a few days later Flight Lieutenant Redpath, leading A flight, intercepted a lone DFW at 15,000 feet returning from a reconnaissance mission. Surrounded by Sopwith Camels and with his observer badly wounded the pilot was forced to land in a field near Adinkerke, behind British lines. The army had already secured the craft and taken the wounded observer to hospital.

"Back the lorry on carefully," said Harry Chisam who had been despatched to collect the enemy aircraft. Two naval ratings peered at the bridge made of railway sleepers that spanned the dyke. Water threatened the bridge directly below.

"Reverse, sir?"

"If the bridge is rotten you'll feel it start give under the rear axle whereas the front will go straight through."

"Aye, aye, sir."

An army officer approached them, "We have the pilot, sir, that's him over there." The man, looking rather young and forlorn, sat on an upturned bucket. Men and equipment circled the plane. An army runner appeared and saluted. "His mate's died. The hospital thought you ought to know immediately, sir."

"OK, thank you; I'll go and talk to him," said Harry

The German stood up as Harry marched over the sodden meadow. Redpath had only landed a few minutes ago running across to the mess and urging Chisam and another two officers to get over to the field. "The army will either blow it up or goodness knows what. It's completely intact. The Admiralty will want to see it."

Chisam had driven over, repeating Redpath's admirably clear directions, as the rating flung the big car across the border into Belgium.

"Do you speak English?"

The German stood up, shook his head and brushed his hands down the side of his uniform. There was an awkward moment – the others backed off. Harry stepped closer.

"Dein kamarade," he said.

"Yes," said the German.

"Dein Kamerade gestorben ist."

"Ich vestehe."

"Is tut mir zehr leid," said Harry (I'm very sorry). Suddenly he and the German shook hands. On impulse Harry Chisam offered him a cigarette. The German produced a box of matches. Together they smoked and watched as the aircraft was loaded on to the lorry and nursed back down the road to Bray Dunes.

Later Breadner inspected the aircraft.

"What a specimen, think it'll fly?"

"Oh yes, sir," said CPO Finch who had masterminded the transport. "We think its radiator's punctured and there are a few bullets holes in the wings and fuselage but we can patch it up and then, well I suppose someone can take it up..." Finch and several other ratings looked enviously at the enemy aircraft. What was it actually like to fly one?

Listening to this, Harry had an idea. Drawing his CO to one side he said, "If it is in fact airworthy, why not let everyone go for a spin in it – should really help morale – we'll have to get used to flying it if we're to take it over the Channel."

"Capital idea," said Breadner "We'll draw lots to see who actually flies it over."

The following day over Thorout, escorting a squadron of bombers with Lloyd Breadner, Harry Chisam dived on five enemy aircraft, some distance below them and simply drove them off. Harry managed to hit two of them; however they retreated still intact. "Returning from the flight we met several enemy aircraft flying in formation – I didn't manage to count how many," said Breadner. "They were after our bombers and attacked them heavily. Chisam getting one right in the centre of his sights fired a short burst. The enemy aircraft went down in a steep dive and then into a spin and was lost to sight. Harry took on several more enemy aircraft but without result." The Albatros DV was marked down as a confirmed hit. This marked Chisam's second confirmed kill. The years of patience and daring were paying off.

After dinner Lloyd Breadner said, "The Admiralty have finally said they want the Hun aircraft. We need to decide who's to take the machine over." Rochford leaned on the mess room piano. Several other officers stood round the stove in the centre of the big tent. The officers' mess was essentially a marquee. "What I'd like you to do is write your name on a piece of paper, fold it in four and put it in this receptacle." Here Breadner produced a captured German pike helmet.

Redpath busied himself tearing up bits of paper. And soon the job was done.

"Right ho, watch carefully – my name's in here too," said the CO.

Breadner stirred the papers in the helmet with one hand holding it with the other. Chisam lit a cigarette. Dipping his hand in he pulled out the first piece of paper. "OK, Redpath, read it out. This will be the pilot of the machine." Redpath unfolded the slip, "It's Tich! Oh I say, Tich Rochford! Are you sure you'll be able to see out of it, old boy?" Rochford was barely five-foot tall.

"Don't forget whoever flies with him runs the same risk."

Redpath stirred the papers this time. Harry thought of the young German pilot, so proud yet obviously distraught at losing his observer. They'd taken him back to the mess for a good dinner and a few glasses of whisky before handing him over to the authorities.

"Harry Chisam!"

"Yes? Good lord!" Pulling the cigarette out of his mouth he took the slip of paper from Redpath and grinned at Rochford.

"Gute reise Tich!"

"Let's make sure the Armament Officer fits a machine gun on the thing, Harry!"

"I'll go and see him right away."

"We've put British markings on it and we'll notify coastal command and Walmer that you're flying across."

Tich Rochford and Harry Chisam were scheduled to fly the DFW over to England on 24th September. However, the day before both were involved in a serious air battle over Middelkerke.

More than 22 enemy aircraft flying from Dixmude over British lines, photographing troops and artillery, had been spotted by ground forces. Harry Chisam dived on one single seater Albatros scout, obtained a good sight and fired two bursts. The aircraft dived heavily and then sped away home.

After an early lunch on 24th September Harry and Tich Rochford took off in the DFW.

"We'll fly along to Calais and then head straight across," Tich said.

"Do it now."

The army, navy and the RNAS stations in Kent had been informed they were coming over. Nevertheless, Harry Chisam swept the sky turning round and looking both below them and above. Rochford flew at a height of 9,000 feet. Visibility was good and once over Calais the pair turned for England and flew straight across the Channel.

The first part of the crossing went well. Then with the white cliffs directly below, a Sopwith Camel flew into view coming straight at them. Chisam caught Rochford's attention  and pointed clearly. Rochford decided to fly straight on, gambling that the pilot had been told of their flight. Chisam, not so sure, gripped the machine gun more tightly and slid the safety catch off. Then he relaxed and shrugged. How could he shoot down one of his own kind? The gun was useless to him. The Sopwith Camel had climbed above them and now commenced its run in coming down slightly above and to their left. A young pilot would probably start firing quite soon. Harry prayed it was an older man who would in any event wait until he had good sighting on their aircraft. That would at least give the attacker time to think. Maybe he'd see their British markings. The Camel droned in, flying straight and level. From a few hundred feet Harry could see the pilot sighting his guns. As he drew near, Chisam, on impulse, stood up. Reaching his hands up above his head he jerked his arms up and down three times. Then he dropped them, jabbing away three more times as the pilot screamed in. Up and down he jumped, remembering the girls at Dayton depot. If only they could see me now. He looked down as the Camel roared underneath them. Rochford flew on unmoved. The Camel turned once more flew alongside them for a few seconds and then peeled off banking heavily away.

The pair landed safely at Dover a few minutes later. The flight had lasted barely an hour.

Rochford walked back to the office in a hut on the aerodrome. "They've given us a couple of Camels to deliver back to Dunkirk," he said airily. "I want to call in at Walmer first – rumour has it we'll be posted there next month."

"Good egg," said Harry.

Leaning on the bar in the officers' mess at Walmer, Tich Rochford said, "Well we made it. I must say that Camel worried me coming right up to us like that."

The door to the mess opened and a small man in flying gear stomped in.

"Good lord, Tich Rochford, what are you doing here?" he said.

"Bob Little! Well I never, I haven't seen you since Hendon."

Bob Little and Tich Rochford had trained together at Hendon Aerodrome. The two shook hands and clapped each other on the back.

"This is Bob Little, Harry, top Australian flying ace – congratulations on the DSO, Bob."

"Oh yes, well, yes, what brings you to Walmer, sport?"

"We're ferrying a couple of Camels back to Dunkirk. Been busy?"

Little scratched his collar; he was still hot and grimy from flying that day.

"Damndest thing; I went up on my own just for a pot shot or two. I saw a Hun machine at about nine thousand feet and thought I'd have him – it was just before lunch – you know an aperitif as you poms might say."

Rochford peered at him over the rim of his glass. "Did you get him Bob?"

"Well no, I had him in my sights and then the observer started jumping up and down, waving his arms. You know I could have sworn he was singing "ugi ugi ugi, oi oi oi" – just like being back on the touch line at school. I tell you what, Tich, that bloody gunner's one of the bravest men I've seen around here in many a moon. I was about to let them have it, when I remembered we had a pair of naval pilots bringing a captured German machine over today. A DFW, I mean, deuce, I'd forgotten. Another drink?"

Bob Little was Australia's top scoring air ace, amassing 37 kills. He was to join Naval Three the following March.

"Ugi ugi, ugi," said Harry and drained his glass.

---

# CHISAM William Hargrove Flight Lieutenant 3(N)

Born in 15 November 1894 in Carlisle, he joined the RNAS as a Flight Sub Lieutenant with effect from 3 January 1916. After flying in England on Home Defence sorties from Walmer, he was posted to Dunkirk and then to 3 Navel Squadron, serving with 'B' Flight from August 1917 until March 1918. He claimed seven victories before he was wounded in the hand during a fight on 26 March.

| | 1917 | Victim | Camel | | Crash Site | Time | | |
|---|---|---|---|---|---|---|---|---|
| 1 | 3 Sep | Alb. DV | B3909 | 3N | Stelhilde | 0730 | OOC | CR/RNAS 3.9 |
| 2 | 11 Sep | Alb. DV | N6364 | 3N | Thorout | 1100 | OOC | CR/RNAS 11.9 |
| | 1918 | | | | | | | |
| 3s* | 9 Mar | DFW C | – | 3N | Henin-Lietard | 1120 | DES(F) | CR/ORB/? |
| 4 | 10 Mar | Alb. DV | B7223 | 3N | E Lens | 1315 | OOC | CR/RFC 10.3 |
| 5 | 16 Mar | Alb. C | B7222 | 3N | Hermies | 1035 | DES | CR/RFC 16.3 |
| 6s** | 21 Mar | Alb. C | B7223 | 3N | 4m E Bapaume | 1645 | DES(F) | CR/RFC 21.3 |
| 7 | 21 Mar | Alb. DV | B7223 | 3N | Beaumetz | 1715 | OOC | CR/RFC 24.3 |

TOTAL: 1 and 2 shared destroyed, 4 out of control = 7
*Shared with FSL J.A. Glen B7185. **Shared with F/Cdr L.H. Rochford B7203, FSL O.P. Adam B3798, FSL K.D. Macleod B7222, FSL J.A. Glen B7185, FSL A.B. Ellwood B7229, FSL C.S. Devereux B7228. FSL L.A. Sands B7216, FSL R.C. Berly B7224, FSL E.T. Hayne B7231.

OOC = Out of control
DES(F) = Destroyed in flames
DES = Destroyed
CR = Combat Report
RNAS 3.9 = RNAS report no.
ORB = RFC report no.

# Kent Respite

"Right, listen all of you, we've been transferred to Walmer – it's an RNAS station above the cliffs outside Deal. The idea is to give us a break from hostilities here," said Lloyd Breadner. "We'll be flying over on the 4th November. The top brass tell me we'll be there for two months."

The aerodrome was on the cliff tops. Officers lived in the village at a house called St Clair. The ratings were similarly quartered in commandeered houses nearby. The naval air station had been created for two reasons – first to offer protection for Dover harbour and the Kent coast, and second to serve as recreation point for naval pilots who had been serving in France without much of a break. Naval Three squadron served continuously from February 1917 until November 1918. Moreover senior RNAS officers realised a great part of the service was made up of pilots from Canada, Australia and New Zealand. Walmer, it was felt, could offer them a look at what it was they were fighting for.

"Kent is called the garden of Eden," Breadner said. "Get out and have a look around."

Local people rallied round. Officers were invited to parties at the Old House in Walmer, the home of the Matthews family. Flight Lieutenant Aubrey Ellwood went on to marry their daughter, Lesley. Earl Beauchamp, warden of the Cinque Ports, was similarly well disposed to the RNAS officers. His wife, the Countess Beauchamp, hosted parties and tennis tournaments. So close was the involvement of the Countess Beauchamp that after the war she erected a memorial to the pilots of the RNAS who had died flying from Walmer. Playing their part with no less enthusiasm were the nurses from the nearby military hospital.

"The object is to kick the balloon," said Harry Chisam. The girls lined up, long calf length dresses, sweeping hair piled up on top of their heads.

"I'm not sure how this helps you fly an aeroplane, flight lieutenant," a timid girl with very dark hair said.

"It's the rudder bar – it turns the rudder on the back of the 'plane. Thing is if you're upside down after a scrap you still have to be able to reach it and kick it right or left."

The girls looked uncertainly at the bright orange balloon suspended from the lampshade in the middle of the mess room. It hung about five feet off the floor. "Here, watch one of us." Aubrey Ellwood, who had been an excellent rugger player, bounced on the spot and executed a perfect drop kick. The first girl, Yvonne, danced up to the ball and did the same. She missed, "Oh bother, it's these shoes." To the delight of the officers Yvonne stooped and tugged off her high-heeled ankle boots.

"Do feel free to remove any encumbrances."

"Steady on, Chisam," said Breadner.

The next girl, Ellie, took a run up and belted the balloon which burst explosively.

"I shot it down, gosh, did you see?" She looked fresh faced and panting. "Bravo!" the men cried. "Let me have another go."

"No it's my turn," said a brunette kicking off her shoes.

Patrolling the North Sea in bad weather with limited visibility demanded no less a degree of verve and daring than active service on the front. However, the occasional mission was flown simply for show. The RNAS, earlier than most, recognised the value of winning hearts and minds.

The tall woman standing at the window looking out over the grey aerodrome turned and said. "Really, commander, I don't know it is safe to send someone up in this."

"It's actually lifting – the main problem with poor visibility is coming into land again," said Lloyd Breadner. "Once airborne we can fly up above the cloud – very pleasant it is, too."

The demonstration pilot knocked on the door and coming in saluted smartly.

"I'd like to see inside the aircraft before you take off, so I can imagine what it's like," said the Countess Beauchamp. Breadner nodded at the pilot. Minutes later Harry Chisam found himself walking the Countess across the aerodrome to his Camel, explaining quite slowly the principles of aerodynamics. The long lessons in the classroom at Redcar had found a use at last, he thought. The Earl Beauchamp, warden of the Cinque Ports, lived part of the year at Walmer Castle but was devoted to the ancestral home at Madresfield at Malvern in Worcestershire. The sorry tale of the Earl's homosexuality and subsequent exile in 1931 and the undoubted splendours of Madresfield would later inspire Evelyn Waugh's acclaimed work, 'Brideshead Revisited'. In 1917 the threat to Great Britain, the Beauchamps, and the freedoms they'd so long defended, lay just across the English Channel, fought for by men like Harry Chisam. The Countess stayed on at Walmer making a statement in its quiet way every bit as eloquent as the speeches in Parliament her husband and his doughty colleagues delivered.

That morning Harry Chisam took off, looped around the aerodrome and flew rather low over the hangars. He buzzed the castle, startling the retainers and gardeners, aware her ladyship was involved with RNAS station.

"You make it look so easy, Mr Chisam," she said as they walked across the grass. Harry had parked the plane alongside a Sopwith Two-Seater 9400.

"You become part of the aircraft, I think that's the secret, knowing exactly what it can do."

"Is it fun, I mean the flying bit, it looks most awfully good fun."

Harry Chisam walked on wandering if she wanted to say anything else. Then he said, "It's the feeling of freedom up there. It's the most wonderful feeling in the world."

"You have to be very brave and daring."

"Would you like to fly?"

"Oh I'd love to more than anything else in the world."

A few days later the Countesss and Harry Chisam met again at a tea party for the RNAS officers at Walmer castle. These were quite regular affairs.

"Mr Chisam, I still think of you and the controls in the aeroplane and I still, well I imagine I'm flying, in my mind. I must sound very silly." To Harry it didn't seem silly at all. One day, he vowed, he'd tell her the story of his sister's blackbird.

"Tell me, your ladyship, what time do you get up in the mornings – I mean do you rise very early?"

"I'm not sure I understand."

"Good time for watching practice flying – the landing strip nice and clear – I sometimes go up for a practice run at six."

*Nurses at Walmer.*

*Countess Beauchamp at Walmer Castle admiring a flypast.*

*Harry with Countess Beauchamp's children at Walmer. The photo was taken by Lettice Beachamp, the eldest girl.*

*Nurses at Walmer.*

*Nurses at Walmer.*
*Harry is fourth from left.*

*Harry with nurses*
*at Walmer.*

"Was that you going up in the two-seater?" Lloyd Breadner asked.

"Yes, I can always use extra flying time, more practice, you know and Finch reckons it needs a spin – just sitting there."

"They're being withdrawn, the 9400s – probably simply be used for training purposes."

"Yes they'd be good for that."

Breadner looked up sharply and said, "Why do you say that?"

---

One morning in December the squadron took off and flew a short distance out to sea. 300 feet below the North Sea surged and ran, white topped, cold and grey. Even this low, the cold was a tangible, constant presence seeking out the unsealed flesh unguarded by cuff and collar. Pilots wore heavy woollen jerseys, thick shirts, undergarments and leather overcoats. Even so the cold blasted into the cockpit, unmoved by the passage of the plane and the ever-shining sun welcoming pilots of both sides to a silver Valhalla above the clouds. The aircraft of the Great War had no heating and were open to the wind and rain. At heights of over a mile guns and equipment could freeze. Putting a hand out to clear them, or even one's face to look, meant the driving wind would ice up flesh and cause frostbite.

This particular morning Naval Three turned inland and droned in low over the downs and the frost-spangled gardens of Kent. Hedges sharp with hoar frost chequered the fields and lanes. Houses with iced roofs loosed vertical plumes of smoke. Cattle bellowing for feed blew great clouds of vapour that hung in the air clearly visible from 300 feet. The practice flight went well, everyone flying in perfect formation, keeping aligned with airspeed deliberately low. A fly-past at 20,000 feet and full speed happens in a second or two. The officers of Naval Three planned to thank the people of Kent on Christmas morning the only way they knew how. In perfect V formation they flew low paralleling the sun which on this the shortest day hung low on the horizon. They flew as the wild geese fly. The leader at the front might change and those of their number crash to a world beneath sunk in mud and despair but on they flew. Naval Three, the thrumming aircraft proclaimed, would never give up the fight to save the fields and meadows below from foreign tread. Neither would they fail the small boys skimming stones across a frozen pond outside Folkestone, nor the cheerful girls putting up holly and fir trees in the Royal Naval Hospital. They flew as a salute to the elderly cottager in Hawkinge and the vicar on his bicycle in Hythe. Far into Kent they progressed, startling a gamekeeper crossing a style near Lyminge, admiring a goods train stood at signals, exhaling smoke at Shepherd's Well.

All returned safely to base to find an enormous Christmas tree in the officers mess. "Chap brought it up on a horse and cart," said a rating called Smith.

"Did he say who it was from, Smith?"

"Said it come up from the beach."

"I think it must be from the Earl Beauchamp," said Breadner.

A Canadian, Carter said, "How come they pronounce it "beecham" – in Quebec we'd say bow shom."

"Good question," said Lloyd Breadner. "The fact is the Normans, who invaded England a thousand years ago, were Vikings who had settled in Normandy. Norseman or Normans do you see? They simply mispronounced lots of French. I'm afraid the British have retained a similar disadvantage when it comes to foreign languages ever since."

Everyone felt discomfited by his mention of an invasion although inexorably fear of it was receding. "Yes, it was 1,000 years ago, the Battle of Hastings, just along the coast from here. And in fact 1,000 years before that Julius Caesar landed at Walmer beach – just down the path – or so they say," said Breadner, ever the scholar.

"Looks like we're in exactly the right place then," remarked Harry Chisam.

———— • • ————

On Christmas morning Chief Petty Officer Wright determined to get out of bed. The side of his face had healed nicely and the stump where his left leg had been was long healed over, even if the flesh was livid and ruddy. The flypast was scheduled for 11 o'clock. Timing would be everything. Once the ward was cleared he peeled back his bed covers to reveal the jersey and row of medals he'd pinned to his chest during the long watches of the night. Taking up his crutches he worked painfully down the ward to the French windows at the end. It took him several minutes. Everyone else would be round the front but he knew there was a good vantage point out here. Quietly he eased the door open. It was very cold outside. However, Wright knew there was no longer much point in worrying about that. The coughing that kept him awake at nights was getting slowly worse and he'd lost an awful amount of weight.

"Where do you think you're going?"

He couldn't wheel round but he recognised the assistant matron's voice, the senior nurse in charge of this wing. "The fly-past – they're a naval flight," Wright said, wheezing.

"You can't go out in the middle of winter dressed in a thread-bare pullover and half a dozen campaign medals, Mr Wright," she said, sailing majestically round his side. He looked at the woman and then out across the gardens again. The door was open and the matron made a move to close it.

"No listen," he said. They paused and together heard the distant thrum of the engines. "It's my old squadron, Naval Three." The noise grew louder but they could see nothing.

"You wait right there, sir, is that clear?"

"What are you going to do?"

"I'm going to fetch you a coat."

Harry Chisam looked down as they sailed in low over the Royal Naval Hospital. Up on a terrace stood a black uniformed senior nurse with a white kerchief shrouding her head. She was partially supporting a man with medals and a coat hung over him standing ramrod straight. The man looked up and Harry stretched out his arm into the slipstream and waved.

"I was with Naval Three in Gallipoli," said Mr Wright. "That's where I lost the leg."

"And won a medal, I believe."

"Oh well that, I pulled a couple of lads out of our scout car when we were hit, I hadn't far to go with them – but, I mean don't tell the Admiralty that."

The unlikely couple walked back into the building and the matron bade Mr Wright follow her down to her tiny office at the other end of the ward.

"Here drink this," she said, turning round from the cupboard on the wall. Wright looked at her suspiciously.

"No it's not medicine, it's finest Madeira." She poured herself a glass.

"Well, this is a great honour, matron."

"No, Mr Wright, let me assure you the honour is all mine."

———————

The Christmas morning flypast lasted forty minutes. Everything went perfectly and the weather was calm. Turning for the aerodrome the aircraft landed one by one and taxied quickly to the hangars. One of the last to come in was Harry Chisam, perhaps a little too fast or too quick in the turn. However, the right wheel of the undercarriage dropped spectacularly, snagged in a badger sett. The Camel jumped wildly and the engine raced. The craft then simply flipped right over. Harry Chisam braced his feet to stay in the cockpit. "High kicking, indeed," he thought, hanging there as it careered round and finally came to a halt. Harry counted to three and lowered himself carefully on to the ground just as Tich Rochford panted up, saying, "You OK Harry, old man?"

"Dropped into my arms like a new born baby," he told the others in the mess as they waited for their friend. Chisam walked in a little later. The officers had all picked up their drinks and Rochford pressed a large glass of whisky into Harry's hands.

Lloyd Breadner raised his glass in salute to his men, "God rest ye merry, gentlemen," he said.

They raised their glasses.

"Bottoms up, Harry!" said Tich Rochford.

For all the men there present that Christmas, 1917, would be one of the most memorable. The Russian withdrawal from the war after the Revolution released hundreds of thousands of enemy troops to fight on the western front. The German High Command knew it had to throw everything against the Allies before the untested might of the Americans was brought to bear. Under the seas the U-boat menace lengthened. A major offensive was being planned for the tortured battle-fields of northern France and Flanders. And in the air too, no quarter would be given.

"1918 will be the longest year of the war," said Breadner.

"How much longer can it go on?" asked a young Canadian.

"Until one side or the other runs out of men."

Flight Lieutenant Louis Bawlf had dressed up as Father Christmas and arrived with the Beauchamp family. Across the room a stony-faced young boy looked accusingly at Father Christmas.

"How did you get here? I didn't see any reindeer."

"He flew in on a Camel," said Breadner.

"Like the wise men," said Harry Chisam.

The boy looked from one to the other and back at Father Christmas. How could he explain that it was all a bit too modern? Could it really be true? He'd asked his grandad for a model aircraft but nothing had happened. The officers and men had gone down to the Royal Naval Hospital and joined the nurses to serve Christmas lunch. One or two of the men had their families down. The children and the patients each received a present.

In the evening everyone went back to the hospital for a concert.

On the train going home the boy cradled the present he'd received from Father Christmas. He kept the wrapping paper and coloured string for years afterwards. He'd stood outside the hospital, talking to a pilot.

"When I grow up I'm going to be a pilot, and I shall fly like you."

"Make sure you come in to land the right way up. Slowly as you can," the pilot said. The boy cradled in his hand a brand new freshly painted model of a Sopwith Camel. Perhaps it was true after all.

*However impressive, naval strength was to be outstripped by aviation.*

*Patrolling the high seas.*

*Harry with brother Sessford and wife Betty in the summer of 1923.*

No. 42

Dated _Jany 23_ 19_18_.

THIS IS TO CERTIFY that Mr. _W. H. Chisam._

has served as _F. Lt._ on board H.M.S. _N⁰ 3 Sqd._

under my command, from the _2nd_ day of _Oct._ 19_17_

to the _23rd_ day of _Jany_ 19_18_, during which period

he has conducted himself * _Entirely to my satisfaction. A_
_daring & resourceful Pilot. Has proved his_
_superiority over stronger forces of the enemy on_
_many occasions. An excellent officer._

_L. A. Bradner_ ⎫ _a/Sqd. Cdr._
⎱ Captain, _N⁰ 3 Sqd._
⎱ H.M.S.

* Here the Captain is to insert in his own handwriting the conduct of the Officer.

No. 22

Dated *March 27* 1918

THIS IS TO CERTIFY that Mr. *William H. Chisam*

has served as *Flight Lieut* on board H.M.S. *No 3 Naval Sqdn*

under my command, from the *23rd* day of *Jany* 1918

to the *26th* day of *March* 1918, during which period

he has conducted himself *In a most satisfactory manner — this officer has had much active service and has invaluable war experience. During the Somme battle in March 18 he made many attacks upon the advancing enemy in the open with great gallantry. His splendid bravery is a fine example to all other pilots and I take pleasure in forwarding this conduct sheet.*

*R Collishaw*
Squadron Commander

Captain, H.M.S. *No 3 Naval Sqn*

\* Here the Captain is to insert in his own handwriting the conduct of the Officer.

"Flight Lt No. 3 Naval Squadron
23rd January 1918 to 26 March
(conducted himself) in a most satisfactory manner. This officer has had much active service and has invaluable war experience during the Somme battle in March 1918. He made many attacks upon the advancing enemy in the open with great gallatry. His splendid bravery is a fine example to all other pilots and I take pleasure in forwarding this conduct sheet.

R. Collishaw
Squadron Commander, RN."

# Return to Bray Dunes

Snow gusted lightly across the aerodrome at Walmer, blown by a gentle yet insistent east wind. Most of the ground crew had gone over to Bray Dunes the day before. The replacement squadron, Naval Four, had already arrived.

"Breadner says we're off after breakfast, immediately," said Rochford.

"I wonder if he'll check the aircraft for girls," said Harry. Several VAD girls had come up from the hospital the evening before, delighted Naval Three were staying one more night. Harry and some of the others had given them rides round the aerodrome in their Camels, not for the first time. Having a girl squeezed into the cockpit made it more than ever a place to be revered, to belong. As Carter put it, to have and to hold.

"It's not just the aircraft he's checking, old man," grinned Johnson, a sunny Manitoban.

Harry decided not to say anything, recalling his last, heated, conversation with the CO.

"Close the door, Chisam. It is essential that we be not overheard."

Harry closed the door, suddenly wondering how serious this would prove.

"I have one question to put to you. Who has been going up in the two-seater with you? Finch won't give anything away. I know you've been using fuel which is fine, I suppose. But he tells me the guns have come back jammed, not once but on two occasions."

"They jam easily in the cold, sir."

"I know that; what I want to know is who fired them and I hardly dare ask, but at whom? The reason, let us be crystal clear, why I am asking you these things is that there is no mention of your dawn patrols in the squadron log. I need hardly tell you it's a court martial offence to take girls joy riding in His Majesty's aircraft."

Later Breadner sat down, croaking out several oaths as he did so.

"Did he return fire?"

"Well he tried to," and then seeing Breadner's expression of near panic said, "No not really, I mean he tried to fly off – I think he was actually quite low on fuel."

Silence fell on the office. An orderly clanked down the corridor outside with a bucket, whistling Tipperary.

"My god man, think of it – a Hun shooting down a, a girl from Walmer – how would it look?"

"She probably shot him down."

"For god's sake, man, why did you do it? A joy ride's one thing but flying out to sea ..."

Harry Chisam thought back to the Edmonton law courts and the carefully constructed defences of the obviously guilty. How could he describe the flush on the cheek of a girl after a dawn flight at ten thousand feet, the sparkle of someone totally alive and relaxed having left the trials of everyday life behind? How could he quantify the benefit that comes from putting your life on the line, engaging the enemy, surviving hostile fire and coming home?

"These girls, they tend our sick, they're utterly committed to the war."

"Oh good gracious, is that it? A reward? What are you telling me now?"

"Oh no, sir, can I assure you, sir, I have acted as a gentleman should throughout this. No, I've seen these girls, very vulnerable, playing host to officers one minute and then looking after young men with their limbs blown off and dying over at the hospital the next. It pulls them apart. To win through you have to reconcile those two pictures – the dead and the living, danger which is no danger at all and security which so often proves false. I know what I did was wrong; it was a gamble, but I know too they have to be strong for us, for the war. It was simply an instinct. I knew it would work– flying – because it's the only way I can understand it. I think that knowledge, that involvement, heals them." He shrugged. "I thought to myself, do it, do it now."

Breadner thought back to his own wife, her bewilderment and the conversations he'd had. How very difficult it was to explain to her the joy and the terror involved in flying.

"It's such a strange war, this war, not like anything that's gone before," he said.

"The world's certainly changed."

"The world, dear boy, is going mad and we're entrusting its sanity to people like you – and those girls."

"Thank you very much, sir."

"No, no, Chisam," said Breadner wearily, "I hadn't meant it as a compliment."

---

Naval Three took off despite low cloud cover and flew directly across the channel as Tich Rochford put it, "dodging snow storms". It was very cold. On landing the officers repaired to the mess tent. Already the ground crew had worked their usual miracle. A stove blazed in the centre of the tent. A teak sideboard sported an urn of tea and a rack of whisky. On one wall hung a picture of the King. Opposite hung the iron cross emblem taken from the forced down DFW.

*Harry Chisam with a souvenir from the DFW captured September 10th 1917.*

Early the next day Harry Chisam took up a new Sopwith Camel on a test flight. The cold was intense. He flew a further patrol with Tich Rochford at lunchtime. On 12th January Harry returned early from a patrol over the coast with a cracked propeller.

"I believe the damn thing froze and cracked," he told the engineer.

Routine patrols followed although few enemy aircraft were encountered that month.

"They're lying low, that's what it is," said Carter.

"Waiting for the spring?" said Harry.

"I don't know; perhaps they've had enough."

"No, they're planning a big attack, a double or quits game. They'll throw everything at us – we know Germany's getting short of food and supplies. The Austrians and Turks have had enough."

"Then there are the Americans."

"I think it would have been better to keep the Russians," said a lanky Canadian.

"No, quite wrong, Russia is in the throws of a dictatorship – it'll be even worse soon. The Americans embody what we're fighting for – British and French values of freedom and fair play."

"They're rather more vulgar about it," said the British officer.

"Exuberant I'd say. They've opened up a whole new continent on just such ideas."

Harry recalled a conversation in a bar in Nancy last year. An American in a brown leather flying jacket with bushy curly red hair was leaning on the bar. He looked as casual as only Americans can. He ordered beer in fluent French. A British army officer waiting to be served said, "Good to see you here – at last."

The American wheeled round, "Been here longer than you, pal."

"Oh I don't think so."

Then he looked at the picture of a Red Indian sown as a flash on the pilot's arm.

"On a scalping party are you?"

"I guess ..."

A naval officer stepped between them. "Escadrille Lafayette?"

"Yeah, bunch of us transferred over from the Foreign Legion – said we could fly."

"And could you?" said the naval officer.

"Not really – did a few flights with a guy in Ohio and blagged my way through."

"So did I, the Wright brothers, my name's Harry Chisam, Royal Naval Air Service."

Suddenly the pilot was shaking hands and the army officer apologised and insisted on ordering and paying for a round of drinks. Harry turned to Tich and Carter.

"They've been here all the way through, the Americans. It was Americans that taught me to fly – the British were far too confused and I went down to Ohio and Georgia – they shifted the school down there when the weather closed in so we could finish our training. Then you look at the French air service, and our chaps and the RFC, there are dozens of Americans flying, hundreds."

"Hardly explains their government's attitude to the war."

Chisam had an answer to this. "The United States is a real democracy – not like ours. If the public don't like something it doesn't happen. Remember half the immigrants to America last century were German. We had to prove this was a war against bullies with coal scuttles on their heads, not a civilised clash between officers and gentlemen."

"Well whatever we think of them they're here now and they fight like fury, I will say that," said Carter.

During much of January it was too cold to fly. Guns froze, visibility was poor.

On 2nd February Harry and Tich Rochford took off together on a hostile aircraft patrol. An enemy reconnaissance machine, an LVG two-seater, had been spotted approaching over Nieuport. The pair intercepted the intruder at 20,000 feet. "We both closed with the EA and opened fire at 50 yards. Harry kept firing as the German drew away and then dived steeply," said Tich Rochford. "I fired 200 rounds and Harry loosed off a steady 300. Both of us had trouble with our guns jamming." It was bitterly cold. The two often flew together during February, although poor weather kept the squadron grounded quite often. Everyone knew the Germans planned a fight back.

"Training's the thing; we need to close with the enemy and shoot down more of him," said Raymond Collishaw, the new squadron leader. Collishaw re-joined Naval Three on 23rd January replacing Lloyd Breadnerm who had been promoted.

"What's he like?" said a rating nervously. "Some say he was pirate operating out of Vancouver."

"He's a cheerful soul, I sailed over with him on the Adriatica – he smiles a lot but he's utterly ruthless – gets what he wants and works hard," Harry said.

Collishaw was one of the highest scoring air aces of the Great War with over 60 victories accredited to him.

Early in February Tich Rochford headed a sizable delegation to the RFC gunnery school at Berck-sur-Mer.

"I say Harry have you seen the beach? It's really good and wide!"

Several afternoons were spent shooting and diving on a balloon towed by a BE2c and a float bobbing about in a pond.

"Take every advantage of this – they can't shoot back. Get as near as you can and then fire."

"He wants us to wait until we can see the whites of their eyes," said Harry.

But there was a point to the lessons. Several pilots were at best getting 10 or 17 shots out of 400 into the targets. "These astonishingly poor results are not our fault exactly but simply mean we do not train to fire accurately," Rochford said. It seemed a glaring admission of poor training but it was true. The air services were still evolving from an observation corps used for ranging artillery and photographing troop dispositions to a weapon in their own right.

"We have to get better at this" said Tich.

"Do it now," agreed Harry Chisam.

One afternoon Rochford heard gunfire from a field behind the aerodrome. Standing in a small group three men were taking it in turns to blast away at a target 75 yards away.

"What're you doing?"

"Getting our eye in. Some of us have not fired a hand gun or a rifle since before the war," said Harry Chisam. "Fancy a go, chief?"

It seemed incredible yet it was true. Pilots with little experience of gunnery were being sent up to take on the German air service.

*The BE2c used for towing a target balloon at Berck-sur-Mer.*

# Mont St Eloi

On 1st March 1918 Naval Three moved to Mont St Eloi, an airfield set up on a ridge northwest of Arras. That afternoon Raymond Collishaw looked down into the valley at the ruins of an old church. How much more of France would be destroyed, swept away? The Germans, he knew, were poised for a desperate all-out push.

Plunging his hands deep in the pockets of his naval duffle coat Collishaw looked back at the neatly drawn up aircraft of Naval 8 squadron, shortly to leave for a well-earned rest at Walmer. Collishaw scratched his chin and turned to the stern battle-hardened figure of his opposite number, Christopher Draper DFC, standing beside him. Under the cowling of each of Draper's Sopwith Camels sat a 150 horsepower Bentley engine. New and faster than the 130 horsepower in Naval Threes the extra power meant better height, better acceleration, and most important of all a better chance in the coming battle. Ray Collishaw looked at the CO of Naval Eight. "I need your machines, Chris. Ours will serve you well enough at Walmer."

Later that afternoon as the shadows lengthened on the frost-metalled ground a lone aircraft took off from Mont St Eloi. Ray Collishaw flew alone. "There he goes, a white knight into the night," said Chief Petty Officer Finch.

Collishaw flew back to Dunkirk and tackled his commanding officer, Charles Lambe, in the officers mess. Draper, understandably enough, had refused to hand over his machines.

"If we take their machines we can fight better, survive longer and ultimately advance the progress of the war – that's the overriding point for consideration is it not?" Collishaw said. Lambe looked up from the table and wiped his mouth with a napkin. He stared straight ahead of him. He knew he was looking at a man who might well be dead in the next few weeks. The German offensive would come as soon as the weather lifted. Naval Eight had done outstanding work undertaking reconnaissance flights high above enemy lines. They were one of the most highly decorated squadrons in the war.

Considering this, Lambe watched as an orderly carried a platter full of potatoes across the room. Would Draper see it as a let-down?

CPO Finch and Harry Chisam walked out on to the air strip late that evening. It was quite dark. Shortly after nine they heard an aircraft engine overhead. "That'll be him, sir," said Finch and shouted an order at two ratings standing by. They sprinted away and oil barrels full of tinder and tar crackled, lighting up the airstrip. Collishaw taxied over to the hangars and as the engine cut and cooled he jumped lightly on to the ground.

"Hullo Harry,"

"Sir?"

"Yes, we got 'em. I'll tell Draper in the morning."

"Do it now, sir. He plans to take off at dawn."

Nearly every day that March in the lead-up to the Ludendorff offensive Naval Three was in the air flying offensive patrols behind enemy lines, sniffing out enemy aircraft on the ground and in the air, escorting reconnaissance aircraft and shooting up supply trains and columns of munitions. The German Air Service now boasted superior numbers of machines and pilots. The Jastas on the western front numbered some 80 outfits almost twice the number of the year before. The Germans poured money and resources into aircraft and submarines, knowing the new weapons of air and sea could accrue victories enough to end the war. Troops and munitions poured back across Germany from the steppes of Russia freed by the Treaty of Brest Litovsk, signed on 3rd March. U-boats stepped up their campaign, slipping wraith-like below the waves Britannia once ruled.

The navy fought on at sea and in the air. On 8th March Harry Chisam and Jim Glen attacked a two-seater Albatros over Feuchy two miles east of Arras on the Scarpe river.

"We poured 600 rounds into the enemy machine, sir, over Feuchy," Chisam told Collishaw as he pulled off his leather gauntlets.

"Did he go down?"

"We drove him down to about 6,000 feet when he turned and headed home."

Glen said, "We chased him as far as we could but he landed under control at Marquion."

"We turned back then, bit of a hornet's nest over there today, sir."

"I know. By the way Chisam, it's pronounced Feuchy – the eu is much softer I think than you've managed."

"Sorry sir."

Enemy air activity increased. The following day, 9th March, Harry Chisam tackled a two-seater DFW over Henin-Lietard to the east of Lens. Fl Lt Glen appeared and between them they brought the aircraft down. The DFW crashed and exploded. Both pilots shared the kill. The following day Chisam went hunting again over the east of Lens shooting down a further enemy aircraft.

"You're having a good time of it, Harry," said Raymond Collishaw, as they walked across to the mess tent.

"That course at Berck helped, that and Tich's practice of getting right up close – had a good sight on both of them."

"Look, watch your back up there. Our intelligence is they outnumber us in the air 2 to 1. The RFC is throwing up boys with hardly any experience and it's killing them. With us we have a great deal of experience and the confidence that goes with it. Never imagine we become impervious to the wiles of the enemy, Harry. Clear?"

The following week saw more flying and the constant drone of enemy aircraft. The weather was dry and conditions quite reasonable. The enemy stepped up reconnaissance. Naval Three flew two flight patrols, a wing of 12 aircraft; six at 15,000 or 16,000 feet with a further flight 500 feet higher and half a mile behind. The aircraft had no means of communication. However, formation flying proved safer and more effective. The Germans, under von Richtofhen, had come to a similar conclusion. Richtofhen also counselled his pilots to avoid stunts, stick together and shoot only at close range.

Nevertheless, Naval Three brought down 14 aircraft in its first few weeks at Mont St Eloi. Harry Chisam accounted for three of these with Art Whealey, Aubrey Elwood and Tich Rochford also scoring doubles. On the 19th and 20th March rain and cloud prevented flying. Then on the 21st Harry scored his fifth victory which qualified him as an air ace. These were five confirmed kills. There were many more pilots and observers mortally wounded; aircraft which crashed on their way home, out of sight and out of control.

# The Ludendorf Offensive

Early on the morning of 21st March the long-awaited German offensive exploded into action. As the front erupted in clouds of smoke, fire, shrapnel and dust the race to beat the Americans was on. France and Britain faced the Kaiser's wrath. However, General Pershing already had 300,000 US troops in France by March 1918 – a number that would swell to 1,300,000 by August. Ludendorff planned to blast a hole in the Allied line at Saint Quentin. Pushing through, the Germans would split the British from the French and drive forward to the north coast.

Chisam woke shortly before five o'clock. Unable to sleep he walked over to the mess. The night watch had tea and he took a steaming mug peering out into the dark. Away to the south he could hear firing. Tich Rochford appeared at dawn.

"Well, this is it Harry, there's more artillery than we've heard for a long time. My guess is they're launching an attack between here and Saint Quentin."

The two officers sipped their tea, imagining all too vividly the hoards of desperate German storm troopers pouring out of the fog. A thick mist blanketed the airfield.

"We'll not be able to get up in this."

"Neither will they," said Harry.

The fog started to clear shortly after nine and the squadron was airborne at 10.15.

Despite the overwhelming numbers of the enemy, Naval Three's B flight, flying at 17,000 feet, saw an array of enemy aircraft below them over Douai. Rochford led his men in a sharp dive holding their fire until they were almost on top of the Jasta. The Camels rolled and soared as the Germans dived and slipped sideways, frantically making height. Guns blazing, the dog-fight lasted until fuel was low and one by one the fighters peeled away, motoring back to base. "Did you see the red triplane among them?" asked Tich, pulling off his leather cap as they walked back across the field.

"I think I nearly flew into him." Harry said.

"I reckon that was our old friend von Richthofen. Intelligence reckons he flies from one of the fields behind Douai."

"Does he?"

Collishaw came in while they were eating a late lunch.

"Well done Jim Glen and Rochford – confirmed kill, that Albatros. Armstrong you had that Albatros too? I need a detail or two afterwards. We're going up again, men."

The officers paused. Tich Rochford wiped his mouth and took a drink of water. "How bad is it, Colly?"

"The Germans are threatening to break through south of here at Saint Quentin. We believe they'll make a push for Amiens. I hardly need tell you what that means for us and the French if we lose the town." It would lead to a split between the two armies and a rupture of supplies. To lose Amiens could mean losing the war.

A and B flight took off and climbed rapidly to 17,000 feet. Although they circled the skies south of Arras they spotted little enemy aircraft and descended to shoot up the lines east of Vaulx. This was a new style of fighting for Naval Three. Collishaw had explained some days ago.

"We need to hinder the enemy advance, stop his supplies – not simply tell the artillery where he is and how short their shells are falling. We've tried bombing behind the lines and for my part I don't think we've developed anything like enough. Anyway the RFC is increasingly of the mind that we shoot up troops and supplies flying low to the ground."

The unspoken thought was that enemy soldiers could shoot back. In a dogfight it was just you and the enemy pilot. Now the infantry would take pot shots at you. "And don't forget old Archie – they'll be able to be a lot more accurate the lower down we are," said Jim Glen.

Few enemy aircraft engaged them. Harry Chisam came in as low as he could on a lane behind the enemy lines. In a field to the left he could see horses and men waiting with carts piled high with ammunition. Turning very slightly he zoomed in low and shot his way through the whole meadow. The horses panicked and bolted. Several were still harnessed and pulled over the fronts of the carts. Others reared and died in the shafts. Men pitched forward, wet splashes of colour welling through their field grey overcoats. Harry flew back up into the air. Another of B flight criss-crossed back over the field. Several German gunners had rigged up a machine gun and were firing back, but it was too late. The field when they looked back seemed very still. The men, reserves, had never reached the front line.

"I could never subscribe to the idea of the glories of war," said Harry Chisam. "To me it was kill or be killed and the violence represented man's final failure. Civilisation indeed." Suddenly flying back across France on a winter's afternoon he yearned for the trees and mountains of Canada, the clean sweeps of rivers and grasslands untroubled by the stratagems of men.

Then just outside Bapaume the flight spotted a lone Albatros two-seater. Together all four aircraft dived on the plane sending it spiralling down to crash well behind the British lines.

"Did you see him land?" Collishaw asked.

"Yes, at least I saw him crash, I think he was pretty much done in before he touched down."

"I want to see if we can retrieve the plane. Remember where it was?"

"It's off the Bapaume road – I could find it I believe."

Together with Chief Petty Officer Finch and Tich Rochford the four of them set off in a Crossley tender. The nearer they came to Bapaume the heavier the sound of firing.

"Looks like the Germans want it back, too," said Finch.

Shells crashed either side of the road. The rating driving the vehicle peered forward through the gathering gloom. The road ahead was lit from time to time with the white light of exploding ordnance. A long column of military vehicles was moving forwards along the road.

"These must be re-enforcements," Collishaw said.

The traffic had come to a complete standstill. A shell whizzed over the road detonating in the field on the left.

"One of theirs I'd say," CPO Finch said.

Another shell crashed down igniting an old oak tree standing in the middle of a field.

"That'll be one of ours," said Finch.

After a while Collishaw said, "We're not going to reach it tonight, we'll turn back."

The following day the Germans had captured the area where the plane had crash landed.

"Looks like they got it back after all," said Finch.

"I shouldn't imagine they'll be able to use it again." Harry said.

On 22nd March Harry Chisam was up flying again early that morning. News of the scale of the assault was alarming but there was no panic. The fighting was fast and furious. Aircraft corkscrewed the very sky, blazing and dancing above the lines. Naval Three fought throughout the day and shot down six enemy aircraft.

On 23rd March B flight took off at 9.30. As Harry revved down the airstrip he smiled as he remembered the briefing. "We've received word to intercept a flight of spotter planes over Armentières," said Tich. "We'll go up to 10,000 feet and see if we can find them. Long sweeps and then home. Clear?"

"No hanging round for mademoiselle then?" quipped Jim Glen.

Rochford found one enemy spotter plane, a Rumpler two-seater, but having a faster engine than the Camel it took off making good its escape over enemy lines.

On the evening of the 24th the squadron flew over Beaumetz and tackled a group of Albatros and Pfalz Scouts at 14,000 feet. Naval Three held formation until the last minute when everyone dived and swept across the rapidly peeling Jasta. Rochford closed right up to an Albatros desperately trying to turn out of a dive and away from his guns. Holding his fire until he was very close Rochford then fired. Although the pilot was not hit the craft was badly damaged and went into a dive from which it didn't recover. Flying back up, keen to regain height as quick as he could, Tich saw Harry's Camel diving very steeply and looked down. Directly below hung a Pfalz Scout heeling over, one wing pointing straight up. Rochford watched as his friend arrowed by, on course flying dead straight at an angle of 45 degrees. The air funnelled past blowing Harry's silk scarf out behind him. Then, just as he passed over the top, Tich saw the guns on Harry's Camel blaze. Tracers poured over the German aircraft and Harry in a split second re-aligned his aim plugging the German cleanly though the middle.

"It was like gutting a fish," he said afterwards.

"Did you see him go down?"

"I knew I'd hit him but I didn't see what happened."

"Well I did; the poor devil never stood a chance, nose dived out of control straight into a field and exploded. So well done. How many's that old boy?"

"The Pfalz will be my seventh. I'm averaging one every couple of days."

"Keep it up, Harry."

But Harry Chisam wasn't destined to keep it up. Neither was Tich Rochford. Both faced the unrestrained fury of the German air service in a 48 hours that was to prove decisive for the war.

The following day, 25th March at 0730 RFC spotters reported huge numbers of enemy troops massing at Bapaume. The Germans pushed hard capturing British soldiers on the roads west, all but paralysing communications. Collishaw spoke at breakfast.

"We've received special orders. All spotting is suspended. The situation is very, very grave. The Germans are, as we speak, forging through Bapaume. We think they're making for Albert. We've been ordered to concentrate on shooting up the enemy as he moves. Low level flying, I'm afraid. Aim for anything you see that moves, horses, camions, carts but above all men. There's a constant stream of reserves simply marching along towards the front. Hit them and hit them hard. Questions?"

No one had any questions. Low level flying had a danger all of its own. Moreover the squadron had hitherto been used to high altitude flying – intercepting enemy spotters escorting reconnaissance.

"OK, we head south to Bapaume and then well, it's happy hunting. Make every burst count."

Low cloud exacerbated the problem but Naval Three took off and headed south. Soon below they could see the masses of German infantry plodding along the roads, looking up appalled at the temerity of the naval men. Tich Rochford had counselled them to dive in a steep angle, very fast.

"Then level out and fire quickly and heavily. Once you've made a pass get up quickly, always turning," he said.

Despite his advice and his lucid thinking, Rochford saw to his horror a rash of holes marching across the top of his wing. A bullet hit his petrol tank and fumes filled the cockpit. Then the engine coughed and died. Harry saw him dive, level out. He looked to see who had fired but there were no EA about. Men on the ground however were firing steadily upwards. A column of infantry lay around the field snugged behind dead horses, invisible in ditches, puffs of smoke marking their fatal signature upon the air. "Switch to your reserve, Tich, do it now," Harry whispered.

Maybe Rochford heard him through the haze of cordite and lead, maybe he would have anyway. But he got his reserve tank open and the engine restarted. Trying as always to regain height Rochford flew off. He had fuel for 15 minutes. Harry turned back and swept in low over the field firing five second bursts, hoping to give Rochford time to clear out. His own fuel low, Harry headed back to the airfield.

Ratings swarmed up to the plane as soon as he touched down.

"Everyone back?" he said. CPO Finch was ordering everyone efficiently and the aircraft was being swiftly refuelled. "I haven't seen Mr Rochford, sir; you're one of the last."

Harry jumped down on the grass and set off over to the mess tent. Coming out of the latrine a minute later he saw Collishaw.

"I'm afraid I saw Tich hit – I think he lost fuel and had to switch to the emergency tank."

"Have you seen him since?"

"No, neither has Finch." Collishaw ran a hand through his hair. His normally smiling face was set firm.

"It's early yet. If he levelled out as you say he could have put down somewhere between here and Albert."

"The place is swarming with Germans, Colly."

"I know, I'll have to tell the ratings to get ready to move if they keep coming."

"I'm going back up."

"Right you are, Harry."

That afternoon Harry saw several tanks – the Germans had very few and had only just started using them in April. Once he was sure they were German, "I thought at first they'd captured ours," he swooped in. Attacks on German infantry continued. Naval Three fought furiously; aircraft returned to Mont St Eloi to refuel and went straight back into combat.

Late that afternoon Harry Chisam spotted another aggregation of troops and vehicles swarming across fields either side of a narrow straight road. A farmhouse marked the start of the build up. Diving quickly he levelled out just 10 feet above the white dust and sped along opening fire straight after the farm. His bullets streamed either side of the road as he gently adjusted the onward passage of the craft. To his left he saw an explosion and felt the bang of it nudging the craft skywards. "Fair enough," thought Harry Chisam and put his faithful Camel B7223, Aileen, into a steep climb, curving at the same time to avoid enemy fire. These were the bastards who had shot down Tich. A cold fury gripped him. Once he had regretted shooting the enemy. Now he felt no such compunction. How could Germany possibly imagine it would hold out against the courage and conviction of the British, the Canadians, France and America? How many more thousands of his comrades had to die before

*Harry, Ally and 'Aileen' in France.*

those oafs in Berlin realised this? Decent men like Tich Rochford, or Lloyd Sands and Will Moyle who had died three days before in a tragic mid-air collision. Knowing he was low on fuel and ammunition he nevertheless looked down at the patient grey figures regrouping in the fields behind the farm. Damn them, go home, get out of France, you fools. Quite unwittingly, he said afterwards, he simply turned and dropped like a stone, plummeting down upon the men. Guns blazing he pulled out of his dive very sharply, the engine shuddering and the white lane was suddenly racing along below him inviting him to see it as a runway.

---

It was a sombre crew who gathered in the mess early that evening.

"I'm afraid Freddie Armstrong's had it," said Jim Glen as Harry came in. All of

S.—1320 b.   (Established—May, 1900.)
(Revised—January, 1917.)

## NAVAL SIGNAL.

FROM—                    TO—

| P.O. of Watch— |
| Read by— |
| Reported by— |
| Passed by— |
| Logged by— |
| System— |
| Date— |
| Time— |

*Back engine bearer shot thro & diagonal (engine) struts holed*
*rear spar of centre section holed twice*
*right aileron & all planes shot holed badly*
*tail plane & elevator shot thro king post of latter carried away, tail skid fitting shot away*
*make & break cap carried away*
*Cowl badly shot, about 20 holes*
*Prop badly splintered*
*Head rest shot through.*

M. 1704.00.
Sta. 6/14.
Sta. 596/16.   *magneto shot – explosive bullet just missing ankle by inches*   885 5 W.50604—D. 68. 32m pads. 2/17. J.T. & S., Ltd. E.878.

"Back engine bearer shot thro and diagonal (engine)
struts holed
rear spar of centre section holed twice
right aileron and all places shot holed badly
tail plane and elevator shot thro, king post
of latter carried away, tail skid fitting shot away
make and break cap carried away
cowl badly shot, about 20 holes
Prop badly splintered
Head rest shot through.
magneto shot – explosive bullet just missing
ankle by inches"

*Harry Chisam's crash combat report and transcript – thousands of pilots crashed and died.*

them had a raging thirst and wanted it quenched with beer and whisky. "Drink water and tea first, you need fluid."

"Streuth, is that an order Colly?"

Harry Chisam sat down at the piano and in defiance of the present gloom struck up. As he played he thought of the men who would never come home. Collishaw watched him and was astonished to see a slow grin spread across his face. Then he looked beyond Harry at the door, wafted open it seemed by the very music...

---

"Bloody hell Rochford, I didn't see you come in. I've just sent off the despatch rider with our combat report and I've listed you as missing."

"Better get him back then!"

Several officers with Collishaw piled out of the mess and set off in hot pursuit. There was a cavalry squadron stationed nearby and two horses were pressed into service to catch up with the motor cyclist.

Later Tich Rochford told the tale of how his fuel tank had been shot out and drained away. "I landed at Lavieville first for another 15 minutes-worth. Then I flew on to Bertrangles. They took ages to help me out – so I had lunch there with Pompy Bartlett – an old pal of mine. Eventually I got off and here I am."

Rochford looked innocently at the officers, some leaning on the piano, Collishaw half-perched on the mess table. "You could have telephoned, Tich."

"Sorry Mum, I did try but I just couldn't get a line!"

"Rochford looked so idiotically young we just started laughing. Eventually Collishaw let lose a great guffaw of laughter and the whole lot of us were barking away. I think it was the tension." Harry Chisam said later.

The Germans had now taken Albert and Montdidier. As the guns rumbled into the night of the 25th the Imperial Army stood just five miles outside Amiens.

The following afternoon Naval Three, after a heavy morning's fighting, decided to fly along the railway line between Bapaume and Albert – this was now in German hands.

The German advance continued. On 26th March 1918 the squadron retreated to Treizennes.

---

Three soldiers picked their way along the sleepers. The air was cold and their great coats did little to warm them. A brick track workers' hut stood at the side of the track.

Maier, the senior of the three, looked inside. A soot-blackened fireplace beckoned. "Come on we'll use those fence posts down below and have a warm." Soon an old chair, judicious use of the tar-scraped sleeper splinters and wood from the pile in the back of the hut had a blaze going. Maier, a resourceful man, put water on to boil. He'd just added coffee when they heard the low drone of an aircraft.

"He's coming from Bapaume; he'll be following the tracks," said his companion, Patiently the three men without speaking unbuckled a heavy machine gun and set it up simply at the side of the hut. Somehow it seemed entirely right that they defend the track workers' hut from air attack.

The aircraft buzzed along at about 200 feet. Schmidt waited until he had the craft in his sights and fired cleanly and simply a short burst. He saw the craft buck and veer suddenly left, away from the firing. Then almost immediately the aircraft started a steep climb.

"He's an experienced pilot," said Maier stepping further out of the hut. Schmidt repositioned the gun as quickly as he could to get off another burst.

"It's too late, you won't get him."

Coming in to land Harry Chisam could see the two hangars and the neat row of tents behind. The engine was coughing and the instrument panel was shot through. He could not feel his hand or his arm. The explosion of the bullets ripping through the narrow cockpit had blocked his hearing. His left eye would not focus either, but the faithful Camel steered as light to the touch as ever. He'd made as much height as he could but knew it was folly to go any higher. This time he felt no anger or fury at being shot. Enemy aircraft had shot at them all this morning but this was no aircraft, he'd flown straight into a careful and experienced German sniper. Damn good shot whoever he was. He could see the white track beneath him and knew he must keep this on his right as he came in to land. He turned slowly over the airfield and he could see the ratings even now looking up at him. They'd know he was hit. The engine sounded different to him. He felt the aircraft shaking and then suddenly knew it was him, not the faithful Camel. He had to get that under control. What had Tich said, "deep breaths, deep breaths and think of a woman or place or something different for a second or two." As if waiting for this, the picture of Aileen sitting in her father's back meadow hit him with a supernatural clarity. Her flesh, pink and young and healthy, the scent of her, apple soap and roses, the touch of her, her breathing lightly on his neck as he held her. My God it would be good to see her again. The aircraft stopped trembling and Flight Lieutenant Harry Chisam lined her up for landing. The tents flashed passed. The other aircraft were parked up neatly and then flaps down he came to rest, kicked slightly and sat there.

Chief Petty Officer Finch came over and he and another rating climbed up on to the wings. Harry Chisam stared dead ahead. "My hands are stuck, I'm afraid Chief Petty Officer."

The rating stepped forward and lent in and put his arm round Harry Chisam. Finch peered at the damaged hand which appeared welded to the joystick. Taking from his pocket a clean handkerchief Finch lent forward and wiped the blood still welling up from a deep wound in the wrist. The bullet had gone straight through. The rating braced himself.

"Hang on blast you, let's not kill him after he's made such an effort to get back to us," Finch said and dabbed again at the hand. With a gentleness not always immediately apparent in Chief Petty Officers, one by one he lifted Harry's fingers clear of the frame. The three of them staggered slightly on the grass and sat the pilot down in the front seat of a Crossley.

"To hospital, right away."

That evening in the mess the officers stood round as Collishaw summed up the situation. "We've succeeded in stopping them for now. God knows how many men the RFC have lost. The infantry have been slaughtered. But I think we've headed the bastards. Chisam's being sent back to England. He lost of lot of blood and his hands are shot to bits; but I think he'll be all right. Finch handled his landing very well. Gentlemen, a toast."

And they drank to their fallen comrades and toasted Harry Chisam unconscious in a field hospital in Amiens. The piano was silent that night.

# Grounded

"I'd like to re-join my squadron, sir."

"Yes I dare say, but ..."

"Look I know my hand means I can't fly, or at least not yet, but there's an awful lot I can do to help."

"I don't see that there is." The officer resplendent in the new RAF uniform looked up. He wasn't unsympathetic but a pilot who can't fly is of no use. He tapped on his false leg and cursed his own grounding. He considered the commanding officer's report he held in his hands. Raymond Collishaw had written, "William H. Chisam has served as Flight Lieutenant on board HMS No. 3 Naval Squadron under my command from 23rd January 1918 to 26th March 1918 during which period he has conducted himself in a most satisfactory manner. This officer has had much active service and has invaluable war experience. During the Somme in March he made many attacks upon the advancing enemy in the open with great gallantry and his splendid bravery is a fine example to all other pilots and I take pleasure in forwarding this conduct sheet."

"Collishaw writes very highly of you. I take his point about invaluable experience."

"We need people on the ground directing operations," Harry Chisam said, leaning forward. "I know Naval Three,

*Convalescing at Peebles Hydro, in Scotland.*

*Officers of the Royal Naval Air Service – note the paper target on the right.*

*Harry (right) on leave with friends.*

sorry 203 squadron, has moved airfields and may have to move again. Keeping that going is important."

"Yes but you're a pilot."

"Maybe but I've worked on farms, I've run factories. I was once part of the Royal Canadian Mounted Police. I know how to organise men and munitions, bumf, supplies, lorries and trains. Heavens my parents are hoteliers. I was raised understanding how battlefields are organised."

"Shame you didn't go into politics, Chisam."

"If I'm there on the ground it frees another fit pilot to fly."

"Royal Canadian Mounted Police eh? Always get your man. Ha! All right then."

"Yes, thank you very much, sir."

Harry Chisam left England the following morning, returning to France, rather pleased the officer had not asked too closely about his apparent logistics background. However he knew he could help, of that there was no doubt whatever. Convalescing in Peebles in Scotland he'd been appalled at the men simply hanging around with nothing to do.

He discussed this with an old friend walking round Russell Square.

"I do miss watching those dawn patrols," she said. "Look I've brought you this." Harry Chisam paused to unwrap the gift, clumsy in his leather gloves.

"My goodness, you've had it engraved, thank you so much," he said, weighing the silver cigarette case in his hand. "I'll fill it up immediately." They stopped at a cigarette kiosk.

"Forty Navy Cut, please."

"Still a naval man at heart," she said.

Harry Chisam tapped the lose tobacco down on his new cigarette case and offered his friend one.

"I have to go back – everyone wants to stop me," he said.

"Of course you have to go and of course it's a danger. I've seen so many of you, being at Walmer, and so many ..." her voice tailed off. Then she went on "Being near aircraft, the smell of aviation fuel, the paint they're always using, the aeroplanes themselves – you're bound to get up in one again – it's absolutely essential."

"Good, I'm glad you think like that too," said Harry Chisam. "That's exactly what I need to hear." It was getting dark and the lamplighters were criss-crossing the streets. Both had different places and people to attend to that evening.

"I wanted you to know, just in case, how much your friendship's meant to me. I can't explain this very well, but it's made me a better pilot."

"I'd never have understood about flying at all if it hadn't been for you."

"All of us are very grateful for your support at Walmer, more than you can imagine."

"Will you fly again?"

"Testing, ferrying, logistics there's plenty I can do. I'll certainly fly again."

"Everything gets so frightfully difficult. Think of me up there, it's where I belong."

In April the RNAS and the RFC had merged to form the Royal Air Force. Many of the naval officers persisted in wearing their naval uniforms for the rest of the war. Harry had been right though – the new service badly needed expert organisation. Much of the logistics soldiers and sailors take for granted were new to the RAF. Chisam was able to establish method and priority as the two flying services merged; because of men like him they still kept flying.

"Have you heard the Bloody Red Baron's been shot down," shouted a flight sergeant as several men bustled through a large chandler's warehouse close by Dunkerque docks. Harry Chisam pushed back his cap. "Where was this?"

"Over the Somme, army says it shot him but one of our blokes had him in the air. Either way it's a great victory."

"All I could think of was the smile and the wave." Chisam later said. Richthofen's last victim had been a man called Lewis. Shot through the fuel tank, Flight Lieutenant Lewis made a forced landing. Richthofen flew right down to 100 feet and waved at Lewis before heading for home. He had now accounted for 80 victories. The following Sunday Richthofen took off as part of a six-plane patrol. Over Le Hamel he met Captain Roy Brown and four other British planes. A furious dogfight ensued. Brown later admitted he didn't expect to survive it. A red triplane suddenly dived on a retreating Camel. Brown turned and brought the triplane into his sights. He was quite close and able to rake the German with fire. The pilot slumped forward but managed to retain control of the aircraft and made a forced landing by some Australian positions. Roy Brown returned to base. It was only later he was informed the pilot, who was dead when the Australians approached the plane, was in fact Richthofen.

That evening Captain Roy Brown went over to see the body. The Australians had laid him out in a small tent and mounted a guard. "He looked so small, so delicate. His cap had been removed. Blond, silk soft hair like that of a child fell from the broad forehead... there was a lump in my throat. If he had been my dearest friend, I could not have felt greater sorrow. I did not feel like a victor."

Perhaps stories of chivalry in the air have been exaggerated. As Richthofen himself said, his job was that of a hunter and he normally took good care to fly carefully, get close and shoot. Allied pilots likewise were ruthless in their pursuit of the enemy.

Richthofen was buried with full military honours. The pall bearers were all RAF squadron leaders. Australian troops presented arms and British airmen laid a wreath on his grave which read, "Our gallant and worthy foe."

---

The summer of 1918 was punctuated by increasingly violent attempts by the Germans to win a major victory before the Americans tipped the balance of power irretrievably. It eluded them. With the arrival of thousands more American troops the Allies were able to mount strong counter offensives. Starting on 8th August the 100 days offensive saw German positions rolled back. When resistance stiffened, the Allies simply cut short their assault and re-addressed their attentions further down the line. Munitions, food and morale among the Kaiser's troops ran low. Ludendorff bluntly told the German government in August that Germany could no longer expect to win the war. The German fleet mutinied in Kiel, thousands of German troops surrendered. Yet the carnage continued. On 26th September US forces mounted the Meuse-Argonne offensive. General John J. Pershing led a concerted push to break the German rail network centred on Sedan in occupied France. In the first six weeks the AEF lost 26,277 killed and 95,786 wounded. Despite his wounds Harry Chisam was back in action again over the front seeking to protect the very people who had taught him to fly in 1915. At the start of October the German government communicated with President Wilson its desire for an armistice. Ludendorrf resigned and the Kaiser was deposed. An armistice was agreed and came into force at 11.00am on 11th November 1918. George Lawrence Price, a Canadian from Nova Scotia, was the last person to die in the war, shot by sniper at two minutes to eleven. He had worked in Saskatchewan where Harry Chisam first started work in Canada a lifetime ago. In France the celebrations were quite restrained. Among the airmen and soldiers there was little of the wild scenes they later heard of in London and Paris.

"We were just grateful it was over," said Harry. The hospitals were still full. Soil was heaped up above a million graves and would take a long time to settle. That day Harry Chisam's mother wrote to him:

11th November 1918

My dearest Hargrove,

Am writing this hoping it will reach you on your birthday and what a birthday it will be, spent under such conditions and in France – when again will you have one like it?

Well darling – this has been a wonderful day of rejoicing and oh, what a relief it is that all this terrible war is over and I can scarcely realise it.
While I am writing, the local girls are parading up and down the streets singing and shouting. All the shops have been closed this afternoon and there has been a huge bonfire with an effigy of the Kaiser being burnt in the Castle Square – you know, just inside the front gate of the Castle where the public are admitted.

My darling boy, God has been very good in bringing you safely through and may He spare you to see many more birthdays and may all you have gone through bring you out in the future a noble and better man. I am glad you are in France at this time. I think you yourself would prefer it. Your dad will have told you we saw Ally passing through on Saturday night. He missed saying when the train was due. He looked well though and sent his love to you.

Now darling I must stop it is post time.

With fondest love and a big birthday kiss – your loving mother xxxxxx

Good night, God bless.

In a cruel twist of fate she was to die several weeks later.

# Hasta la Vista

"Will you go back to Canada?" Ally Shaw said as they drank tea outside the castle. Shaw had a job fixed up in London; he would go on to live in Dover.

"I've been thinking of joining the oil industry. Think it through. We all know how to take apart and rebuild an aircraft engine."

"They're getting much more complicated now, you know."

"Yes, but the point is we understand the – what do they call it? The internal combustion engine. We know all about it, how it works, what it does. Look at the cars and aircraft we're producing now. They all need oil. Liquid gold, Lloyd Breadner called it."

"What are you two plotting now?" The Countess Beauchamp came across the lawn from the tennis courts. The two pilots had leapt to their feet.

"Harry wants to join the oil business. Says his squadron leader told him to."

The countess looked at Harry Chisam and on impulse ruffled his hair. It was a familiar gesture, she'd become much closer to the pilots at Walmer than she'd realised. Now it was all over. All of them sat down again.

"It's different for all of us. I have no particular wish to go back to Canada, not when so many people I flew with won't be going back."

Conversation stalled. The Great War, as it became known until 1939, robbed a generation of its ease and purpose.

"If it's a help, I think I know people who can talk to you."

"Oh no, I'll be OK."

"That's a good idea," said Ally Shaw. "Just do as the lady tells you," and he winked at the countess which delighted her. Shaw had to leave to catch a train. Harry Chisam and the Countess Beauchamp walked back across the tennis courts. "Thanks so much for the snuff box," he said.

"Well, that's very kind and such a kind note you sent."

"Why did you send me it? You've been so generous," he asked.

The pair of them stared out across the sea. Children were playing in the garden, running through a rose arbour. She said, "So many of you went away and I tried so hard to, you know, to not worry or think about it. So vulgar to fret. But you, you came back, you see." Then this towering strong woman gulped and sneezed explosively.

Harry Chisam pulled out a clean handkerchief – which all pilots carry for precisely such emergencies.

------◆◆------

When the Great War finished Harry Chisam went to work for the oil industry in Mexico until 1931. Instead of flying light aircraft he tramped the oil fields on mule back, running gangs of oil drillers and roughnecks. The work was hard and often dangerous. Oil wells exploded, caught fire and killed people. Compared with the horrors he'd witnessed in France, Mexico held few terrors for him.

Chisam found a world which squared his conscience – the searing heat, the risk

*Well-head fires made oil drilling
highly dangerous.*

*Living conditions could
be very primitive.*

*Oil workers take a break*
*and pose for the camera.*

*A family picnic in Mexico*
*in the 1920s. Harry is*
*closest in the foreground.*

*Harry at work in the
oil fields, Mexico,
November 1922.*

*A lonely road in Mexico.*

*Mexico: Pobero oil camp
house 'Hacianda' in 1922.*

of attack by bandits, the blowouts on oil wells and the long hikes up mountains and across deserts. Just as before there was the added responsibility of getting pay and rations to the men under his charge. Learning Spanish helped him in his work; quite often American and British managers never troubled to learn the language. But Harry Chisam could speak it with a confidence and a fluidity born of earlier attempts at French, German and Flemish. Half-understood idioms he used delighted his staff.

Oddly enough experience gained with the Royal Canadian Mounted Police was put to good use amidst the scorched sierras of Mexico's oil fields. Justice, Harry Chisam once remarked, is not the preserve of the cool and the calculated. At the end of every day he showered in the rusty water behind his white hacienda and then he would go out on to the veranda and pour himself a cold beer or a long scotch and sit down. In time he stopped waiting for the mess dinner gong to boom or for the drone of a late returning aircraft. But the whisky tasted just as it always had and he understood as a non-drinker never can the properties of the spirit, and the reason the Gaels named the drink *uisge-beatha* – the water of life.

Chisam worked an unremitting seven-day week taking a couple of days off every once in a while to visit Tampico – a boisterous sea port. Many years later a friend in the oil industry recalled, speaking of his career as a whole, "He had the knowledge of life and of men and women that all persons ought to have – and few have. He had endless patience – no individual problem was too small to claim his undivided attention in the heat of a busy day. Always he would be ready with unwearied kindness and wise counsel, leavened with a sense of humour." Harry Chisam was a good listener and a man of immediate action.

*Pipeline laying
in Mexico.*

Henrico, the porter at the Hotel Tamaulipas stepped out on to the street and looked up at the first-floor wrought-iron balconies. Behind an open full-length window a woman had screamed. He heard a long "No!", then a gasp and the crash of a vase. Uncertain what to do Henrico went back inside. Most of the noise from the hotel was lost on the busy Calle Juarez, but she'd screamed loudly. That would be the way of it – an early evening honeymoon couple, he thought, striving to remember the elderly bear of a man who had turned up with the more refined girl at least 20 years his junior in the beaten metal heat of the afternoon. Tampico sits beside the ocean, the point of departure for ships and lovers alike. Perhaps the odd couple were off to travel abroad. The thought of the thickset man and the girl flustered him, making him feel guiltily erotic. Money, that was it, money paid for everything – even freedom.

"You promised my father we'd wait until we were married next month."

"What difference does it make, Celestina? A week, a lifetime? You madden me."

Suddenly Celestina Gloeckner blinked her large brown eyes and decided that a lifetime was too long a repentance. Her fiancé, their next door farmer, Rios, turned solemnly and locked the hotel door.

Why was her mother not here? Perhaps she had colluded in this. The girl never considered giving in. She wouldn't do it, not now, not ever, not with this oaf. Steadying her breathing, she came to a decision.

"You must wait, I must get ready." She gestured at her adjoining bedroom. "Give me ten minutes. I will be ready for you then. I must ... I must prepare myself."

Rios, a simple man, looked at her again. He really couldn't wait a minute longer. She drew a deep breath and pressed her hands together in front of her strained chest.

"It will be better in ten minutes. I am frightened; but you give me strength."

He nodded once, very briefly and she went into her room.

Celestina strode quickly through to the windows and stepped out on to the balcony. Taking a deep breath she prepared to climb down. Aware someone was watching her she saw a man in his shirt sleeves on the balcony next door smoking a cigarette.

"I wouldn't jump down. It is too far, you could kill yourself."

"I thought maybe I could hang down from the rail – then drop."

"Why not just walk out the hotel this way," and he swept his hand back across his own apartments.

Thirty seconds later she found herself sitting in a chair sipping a glass of whisky

*Harry Chisam was a good listener.*

and telling this oddly sympathetic stranger why she had run away. Her father was very poor and his friend, a richer man, wanted to marry her. The man's first wife had died some years previously.

"It's the age-old story – St Nicholas and the miller's three daughters,' he said and smiled.

Celestina nodded uncertainly.

"Where will you go?"

"I will disappear into the city, I will find work and save money. Then I will go to New York – I have family there, my grandfather's other people."

"Finding work might be more trying than you imagine. How strange – I have just come up from the harbour and an old friend of mine this afternoon."

The man sat down at a small desk and started writing. He wrote several letters as she shuddered and sipped the whisky.

"I keep shaking."

"It's shock – I see it all the time after an accident. Take deep breaths; it'll pass."

"Do you work in the oil fields?"

"That's right, 12 hours a day, 12 days in a row and then two days here."

"I'm taking up too much of your time, senor."

"That's quite all right, I rarely welcome beautiful girls into my room as they bound from balcony to balcony."

Then he held his hand up to reassure her.

She looked around the room at the pictures on the table of two parents and their four children. Then she saw pictures of men in uniform and a row of aircraft neatly drawn up on a field. Finally her benefactor stood up.

"These are letters giving you safe passage on the Richmond. She sails tonight for Savannah, Georgia and then up river to Augusta. From there you can go by railroad to New York. You must cable your friends from Augusta, understand?"

Only then did the two introduce themselves. Celestina said, "Gloeckner is a German name. It means a ringer of bells. I'm so sorry and you have been so kind. My grandfather was from Germany. You are English, senor?"

"Yes I am."

"You must hate them."

"Oh no, not really, I have known several Germans and they were all very brave. Just like you."

The man gave her the letters and an envelope packed with US dollars. Celestina Gloeckner shook her head.

"I can't take this, why are you doing it?"

"I have walked through your square, Plaza de Libertad, many times. I'd like you to take this. I fought a war so you could go on calling it that; please, just do it."

"I cannot get out of the hotel, they will be looking for me."

"Nonsense, a little ingenuity and an old coat and hat."

Later Henrico gallantly opened the door as the bald headed Englishman trod carefully on to the street leading a very old lady well wrapped up despite the heat. He must be older than he looked – of course he hadn't really seen the English man without a hat. How bald he was! Strange how they aged better than the Mexican women that so many married.

The following morning a banging on the door disturbed the man as he poured his coffee. The hotel manager and several embarrassed-looking police in ill-fitting uniforms came in.

"Can I ask you, senor, if you have seen this girl, a guest of the hotel? She was in the rooms next door? She has disappeared and, well ..."

The manager handed a carefully posed portrait of Celestina Gloeckner.

Studying it the man handed it back to the hotel manager who had spoken in careful English.

"I'm afraid not," said Harry Chisam. "Can't say it rings any bells."

---

Trips home were conducted in some style. Chisam travelled first class on the liners to and from Britain. As one colleague said, "He worked extremely hard, to the detriment of his health really, but he'd drink and ride and shoot with a passion that only those who have looked death head on and stared it down can imagine." Yet despite his abiding sense of loss at the effect of the Great War he bore his adversaries no ill will. Many evenings were spent playing poker. Chisam had that rare ability of holding out and stopping when he was ahead. Most of his first class trips back to England were paid for by his winnings. Life was for living to the full. Chisam delighted in taking his sisters, Edith and Elsie, to Ascot and Henley for trips to the theatre in London. They dined at fine restaurants and travelled first class by train.

Travelling back by train from London, Elsie said, "I do so like it when we're all together like this ... honestly Hargrove it's very good of you to treat us. Much Ado About Nothing ... I think it's one of his best plays." Her brother stared out of the window at a group of men digging in a field. They were excavating the footings for a new house. The criss-cross pattern of the trenches was familiar. "I couldn't begin to tell them I too wanted to be in their company. Perhaps I didn't understand myself," he once said years later. Instead he let the rocking motion of the train comfort him. "You wrote me so many good letters in France, both of you. They kept me going. I suppose I wanted to pay you back. I'm not a very good writer."

"Oh yes you are! You write wonderful letters," said Elsie.

"He's just a show off," said Edith. "Prefers to get Shakespeare to do all the hard work."

---

The poker school had been playing since mid-afternoon. Most of the men had declared after dinner. Captain James looked in on them again at midnight on his way to the bridge. Von Neubrucke was still there looking ever more grave, a sad figure in his white duck suit. Two of the Mexico oil men played on, almost oriental in their motionless devotion to the game. An American from Pittsburgh, he thought, had stayed the course. When next the captain looked in a steward was serving fresh drinks and the winner of the game had ordered French champagne. Everyone relaxed. The language of the room was English. "I salute you. Mexico is not a country I associate with winning," Von Neubrucke said.

One of the Mexicans in very broken English replied "Neither is yours. We fool you that we are poor, poor in politics, broken by civil war but no, we're rich."

"Hell that's not how we look at it," said the American. "We're the winners; I mean look at the war."

Von Neubrucke looked up sharply. "You didn't win the war, we signed an armistice."

The American snorted – he'd lost a great deal of money. So, at least, had the

German. The other Mexican, the quiet oilman who had won, finished counting his winnings – it had taken him a considerable time. But he liked the champagne and decided to order another bottle. The steward spoke to him in Spanish and the man laughed. Leaning back in his chair he hooked his left hand in his waistcoat pocket and put a cigarette in his mouth, lighting it with his right hand. On impulse he leaned over and offered the German a cigarette from his silver cigarette case. Von Neubrucke found himself relaxing under the man's ready smile and the champagne tasted very good. Losing at poker didn't matter so much, not when you were as rich as he and not when you'd lost a war. At least, he consoled himself, the wretched British were not involved in the game. Raising his glass he said, "Zum wohl."

Despite throwing himself into a busy career as an oil explorer Chisam admitted he was lonely. Few people could understand what he'd been through.

"We're putting you in charge of river transport," said the American agent.

"I don't know anything about boats."

"Hell you do, says here someplace you was in the navy."

Many who had fought and survived the war carried within themselves a gap left by the fallen, a sense of undeserved good luck, an irredeemable promise. Once representing an asphalt company in Mexico he flew to Guatemala to negotiate a million-dollar contract with the President. Ten days later he returned and advised his company not to go ahead. "Guatemala was in turmoil," he said. The President was shot dead by revolutionaries three months later. "I formed the impression when talking to the man that he'd used all his good luck up," Harry Chisam said.

In 1931 he returned to Britain and became a branch manager of the Dominion Motor Spirit Company in Leeds. He would go on, years later, to win a poker game organised in the 1950s to raise funds for the Moortown Golf Club. Good luck did not desert him. "I am pretty sure I have forgotten how to play," he told the Secretary. "Just do what you can, Chisam," the secretary said in an unconscious imitation of Lloyd Breadner. 24 hours later the Secretary said, "You cleared the table – can't think how much better you could have done had you remembered."

One evening Ally Shaw arrived at Leeds station taking a detour to see his friend en route to Stranraer and the ferry to Belfast. The pair met in the hotel where Harry was staying. Sitting in the lobby Shaw happened to look up at a movement on the stairs at the other end of the long room.

"I say, Harry ..." But his friend had already seen the two girls in their cloche hats and fashionable calf-length dresses, descending.

"Remember the drill, wait until you have a good sight on them. Don't go off too soon or you'll miss," said Ally. Harry Chisam remained dumbstruck amidst the early evening bustle of the hotel. A page boy skidded over the parquet floor. A small man with a huge moustache sailed imperiously across the floor and rang a bell on the reception desk. A clerk looked at him over his spectacles. In the next room a piano player flexed his fingers and pinged too high a note.

"Target closing thirty feet, safeties off, old boy, twenty feet ..." Shaw kept up the commentary.

"I'd not seen him so thunderstruck since the soap factory blew up," Shaw later recollected.

Chisam simply stared at the girls. The one on the left had long eye lids and seemed to be looking down, self effacingly, letting her friend do the talking.

"Ten feet and a very good sight." said Shaw.

As the girls drew level he suddenly stood up.

"Oh do be careful ladies, the floor's still wet. The chap with the salsa, don't you know, slopped vinaigrette all over the floor." Shaw pointed at the immaculate parquet, still polished and gleaming despite the day's traffic. "Yes they cleaned it up but it's a bit slippery. Would you like a hand?"

"Actually we're waiting for someone..." said the more outgoing of the two girls. Unbidden Chisam stood up, still staring at her companion.

"Oh well, do please join us. We'd be honoured," said the ever gallant Shaw.

The two girls looked at each other and then sat down. It was such a public place, what could happen?

"Guns jammed old son?" Shaw said out the corner of his mouth.

"Can I order you some tea?" Harry croaked.

"No, thank you, really we're being collected directly."

Shaw introduced himself and Harry. The girls admitted they were called Millie Appleby and Ethel Skidmore. Both were staying at the hotel and were involved in selling clothes to the retail trade.

"We specialise in bringing good clothes that make pretty girls look prettier," said Millie.

Shaw said that must be hard work.

Ethel put her hands together cheerily, "I don't know that I'm necessarily very good at it."

"You're better at it than you could ever possibly imagine," said Harry Chisam suddenly. She looked up into eyes that had raked a thousand miles of empty sky without finding what they searched for. Then a waiter approached them. "Captain Chisam?" Harry took a note, a message from the duty petroleum manager out at Tadcaster.

"Are you in the army?"

"No, we were naval men, well, Royal Air Force, during the war."

"Oh did you shoot down many Huns?" Millie gabbled.

"He did, he's an air ace. Don't ever mention the name Harry Chisam in Germany," said Ally. "People dive for cover, empties whole restaurants, waiters hiding under tables, frightful business ..."

The girls were met by a bald man striding across the floor. Millie greeted him over enthusiastically while Harry, at last pulling himself together, spoke to Ethel.

"Will you meet me tomorrow for tea? Here?"

She pulled the back of her hat down, looked up and tried to smile. The man opposite her frightened her with his intensity.

"If you're sure it won't be too dangerous Captain Chisam ..."

They were married three months later.

"Just remember, I forced 'em down, old boy," said a jubilant Ally Shaw as he clambered aboard the train, "Just like that DFW – nothing to it ..."

*Harry and Ethel met while both living at the Mount Hotel in Leeds. This photo was taken in 1932, and they were married in 1933. Tony was born in 1934 and Margaret in 1936.*

# Madresfield Revisited

It is given to few men to fall happily and completely in love. Fewer still build a marriage which withstands economic discord and a major world war.

"I didn't know you knew the Countess Beauchamp so well," Ethel Chisam said opening the wedding presents. "She's sent a whole Worcester china breakfast set."

Harry Chisam laughed and looked at his young wife. "I came to know her and the family very well when I was stationed at Walmer. They took a real interest in us and helped us very much."

Ethel and Hargrove went on to have two children, Tony and Margaret, the co-author of this book. Too old to fly, Harry Chisam served in the RAF as an Intelligence Officer during the Second World War. Occasionally his children remember him turning up at the dead of night, a comforting figure in the blackout. Food parcels from old girl friends in the United States arrived throughout the war.

"That's the Americans for you, always like to help – they're the most generous people in the world," said Harry Chisam. If marriage and a family stayed his wanderlust, it never stopped the long drives across England or the lonely walks in the hills of Cumberland and Yorkshire. Hot Mexican food remained a life-long passion. "It's just a few beans and chicken and chilli," he said innocently as Ally Shaw spluttered over dinner at Norse Range one night. Shaw reached for a draught of cold beer. "Bacon and cabbage at my place, next time, old boy." Visiting Ally Shaw near Dover was a bi-annual pleasure. They were godfathers to each other's children. Both men would take the children paddling on the beaches they had helped keep safe for so long. Chisam finished his career with the oil industry. Breadner's prediction had kept Harry gainfully employed until his retirement.

Raymond Collishaw and Tich Rochford went on to play major roles in the RCAF and the RAF respectively. The Earl of Beauchamp died in New York in 1938. The Countess died in 1936. The Beauchamp scandal broke in 1931 and the Earl, his homosexuality revealed, fled into exile, returning to Madresfield only at the end of his life. Harry Chisam visited the Countess during the 1920s and 1930s in London and at Madresfield. They shared a bond that mystified friends and families. The Countess remained a devout High Anglican, deeply affected by the Great War.

When she died service personnel were prominent among her mourners. Although a strange and aloof woman – on poor terms with many of her family and heart broken at what happened to her husband – she nevertheless commanded an affection and respect among air force personnel at Walmer which has never been adequately reported. Among the many tributes to the Countess was a small floral wreath with a message that puzzled those who bothered to read it:

"To a brave and daring defender – free at last. Per Ardua Ad Astra, HC."

---

"Daddy, you didn't tell me there was a moat."

"Yes, it's designed to keep enemies out and friends in."

Madresfield in 1950 still sparkled, the red bricks catching the sunshine, the fields loud with cattle.

"Be careful," said Ethel Chisam. In fact Margaret, her daughter, could wander off at will along corridors and through rooms, the galleries shot through by a sense of the past and what might have been. "My brother was at Malvern College nearby and we had driven over to take him to tea at Madresfield. The then Earl, who Daddy had known as a boy, and his Danish wife invited us over."

It seemed a sad place that afternoon, yet was still full of tolerance and kindness. Margaret picked up a kitten. "It was a white kitten and straightaway the Countess, Mona, asked me if I'd like to keep it. Mother said no.

"As we walked in the garden my father sensed something of my feelings about the house. Sad, empty really, for the last Earl and Countess Beauchamp had no children."

"You have to keep trying, keep on top of life, it's very difficult but it's making the effort that counts. Do it now! So many people cannot because they're dead, they died too young. That's our responsibility, to live life." The two had broken off from the main group. Margaret would be going back to Seascale to Calder Girls School. Her father would write to her every single day during the School Certificate exams. "He believed in encouraging people. Every day he'd say you can do this, you're better than you think. In a way he flew me through those exams."

Chisam was always close to his two sisters. Elsie married Watson Bell and had two daughters, Sheila and Nancy. Going to their home and taking the girls out for ice cream was another family custom. "I can't go into one of these new ice cream parlours without thinking of Nancy getting it on her nose," Harry Chisam said.

Sadly his beloved wife, Ethel, died in 1954. "It broke his heart," says Margaret. Ally Shaw remained more optimistic. "He found someone he truly loved, someone finally who gave him a reason to come home. Harry never talked much about what he did in the Second World War, all very hush-hush. He was in Military Intelligence, but I remember he would get home as often as he could. Any question of leave in London or meeting up was usually tempered by his need to be with his family."

When he retired Harry Chisam returned to Carlisle and lived with his sister Edith. Sadly Elsie had died much too young, although her daughters, his nieces, Sheila and Nancy, continued to delight him for the rest of his life. Harry Chisam died in 1972, aged 77.

---

That afternoon in Carlisle Edith answered the door. "Well, full circle then, Hargrove," she said as he carried his cases in. Most of his effects would follow by van. Among them the photographs, letters and aviation reports on which this book is based.

"Come on inside, I'll make tea." Harry followed her, his feet crunching on the path. It reminded him of that last afternoon at Madresfield.

"Come on," said Harry Chisam to his daughter as they crunched up the gravel behind the great house. "I want to show you a sundial."

"A sundial?"

"Yes, there it is. Now look what it says. Read it very carefully and remember it always."

The inscription on the sundial, which is still there, says, "The day is wasted on which we have not laughed."

*Margaret with Ivonette Miller and her husband in 1985. She was the Wright brothers' niece – the nearest relative as neither of the Wright brothers married.*

*Memorial at Dayton Ohio. Margaret in Dayton 1985 pointing to Harry's name on monument to the early flyers. See page 33 for a closer view.*

*Margaret in front of Wright B Flyer plane holding a photo of her father in his Wright B Flyer. Dayton 1985.*

# Epilogue

"Well I had a few, sergeant major, I admit, I had a few."

"A few? I should say so. I saw you fall over, laddie."

Aircraftman Foster stared through the evening at the NCO, fire breathing and clearly annoyed. He'd counted on the two-mile walk back to the camp to sober up. Now the Sergeant Major had spoilt it all, banging out of a cottage directly in front of him. The two men peered at each other. "You're a bloody disgrace. And you're on a bloody charge."

Just then a staff car purred up the street. The NCO willed it to go away. However, the car pulled level with him.

"Good evening sergeant – need a ride back to the camp?" Oh great heavens, an officer, just what he needed. An officer spotting him climbing out of Maesie Whitfield's window and stopping to ask if he wanted a bloody lift.

"No thank you, sir, walk'll do us good, sir."

"Your pal doesn't look too well, sergeant major."

"He'll be all right thank you very much, sir."

"I doubt it sergeant, there's a posse of MPs down in the town. They'll be patrolling this road like as not." Breathing deeply, the man was only trying to help after all, the NCO jerked his head at the owl-eyed Foster. "You hop in the back and bloody well behave yourself? Clear?"

"Yes, sergeant major."

Foster slid gratefully on to the red leather seats and gripped the door handle. Prudently he lowered the window and gazed vacantly out across the night. He must have dozed off. A roar of NCO laughter roused him. The officer and the sergeant major clearly knew each other. Relieved, Foster hunkered down again, comforted by the smell of leather and the pungent tobacco from the front. He couldn't articulate it but the men in front oozed re-assurance.

"Oh yes, I made it to France, spent most of the war there. Flying Pups and then Camels." The NCO muttered something. The officer said, "What all of them? Gordon too?"

"Yes sir."

They drove on quietly.

"Could you drop us 100 yards short of the main gate, sir? Frankly neither of us is supposed to be out. Laddo there won't make it past the guard room."

"Yes of course."

Suddenly Foster hiccupped, he felt sober but the motion of the car had set him off. The Sergeant Major wheeled round, "Bloody Hitler must look at people like you, son, and realise he stands every chance of winning."

The car stopped and all three men got out. The officer passed cigarettes round. The RAF was like that, rather less formal than the other services. The officer laughed to himself. He leant back on the car with his cigarette in his left hand. "I hear old Mr Hitler doesn't drink alcohol, not a drop."

"I heard that, too," said the sergeant. Foster tried to stand up straight and said, "Sorry sir."

"No need to apologise for the leader of the Third Reich," said the officer.

"Beer and girls, eh, Sergeant Major?"

Far away in the sky they heard a squadron of bombers gaining height, heading for Germany.

"I wonder where that lot are bound for," said Foster. He hoped the clouds would hide them from the Luftwaffe.

Harry Chisam looked up at the sky and checked his watch. He knew where they were bound, but of course he couldn't say.

*Harry, Margaret and Tony*
*on Seascale beach,*
*Cumberland, in 1937.*

# Author's Note

Some of this story is based on anecdote and conjecture. However, I have followed as nearly as I can the career of Harry Chisam in the RNAS and RAF. The pre-war adventures in Canada are all based on fact, including the factory explosion in Saskatchewan.

Amazingly pilots had to pay for their own training in the early part of the Great War. Harry Chisam and Ally Shaw both trained at the Wright Brothers' Flying School in Ohio and concluded their training in Augusta, Georgia. I can only surmise Wright did this to help the war effort. Chisam met President Wilson on his way back to Britain. The details of the crash in Yorkshire are a matter of record. Chisam then went on to serve in Scotland.

However, the clearest picture we have of his career is from the logs of Naval Three squadron. Harry Chisam engaged the enemy over northern France, Belgium and the North Sea many times, almost dying as a result. He really did flip his plane over on landing on Christmas Day at Walmer. He crash-landed on the beach near Dunkerque and was shot down over the Somme. The friendship with the Countess Beauchamp is intriguing. She certainly gave him gifts and befriended both Chisam and other officers stationed at Walmer. She remains a much misunderstood woman. She helped set up the RNAS memorial at Walmer after the Great War. Chisam visited Madresfield several times and took his daughter and son to tea there in 1950.

Did nurses from Walmer fly? We know they were given rides around the aerodrome. I have tried to emphasise their importance and that of the ground crew. Mr Finch really did exist. So often these people go unpraised. Chisam and Rochford flew a captured DFW over to England and were nearly shot down by Bob Little – whom they met later that day.

The horrors of the Great War and the bravery with which men faced it defy adequate explanation. Chisam had a strong desire to serve his country and was unwavering in his determination to do so. Interestingly he bore the people he fought no ill will.

Details of his career in Mexico are harder to come by – he was an excellent poker player and he worked hard in the oil fields. Chisam had an eye for a pretty girl. He was devoted to his wife, Ethel, and became a committed family man and an accomplished letter writer and, as we have seen, a good photographer.

In 1985 and 1995 Margaret Partington, Chisam's daughter, travelled to Dayton, Ohio and met the Wright brothers' niece, Ivonette Miller Wright. Harry Chisam's name is engraved on the plaque commemorating the pioneers of aviation trained by the Wrights.

The story of Harry Chisam and the men he served with has slipped imperceptibly into history. May this book with all its imperfections serve as a thank you and a salute.

*Andy Milne*
*Hereford*
*October 2008*

THE GUARDIAN ANGEL    *Eleanor F. Brickdale, A.R.W.S.*

*This picture was always in the family home. Margaret still owns it and thinks that the angel guarded her father's plane safely through the Great War.*